Now his fingers were pressuring over the skin inside her wrist again and she wanted to snatch her hand away, but he tightened his grip, pulling her a centimetre—no, more—towards him. It was enough to render the distance separating them as nothing. They were virtually in each other's arms. His lips hovered over her forehead. She had to raise her face in order to see what he was going to do next. What she saw in his eyes made her catch her breath.

'When my kid brother turns up with a blonde blue-eyed actress on his arm, and apparently engaged, I'm naturally inclined to think the worst,' he told her, scarcely moving his lips. He was so close, so close. She could see the minute bristles on his jaw, imagined, before she could stop herself, the rough male touch of them over her skin.

Oblivious to these thoughts, he went on, 'You're a very beautiful young woman.' He lowered his head a fraction. 'And Peter's such a boy.'

CASTLE OF DESIRE

BY

SALLY HEYWOOD

MILLS & BOON LIMITED
ETON HOUSE   18–24 PARADISE ROAD
RICHMOND   SURREY   TW9 1SR

First published in Great Britain 1991
by Mills & Boon Limited

© Sally Heywood 1991

Australian copyright 1991
Philippine copyright 1992
This edition 1992

ISBN 0 263 77437 6

Set in 10 on 11½ pt Linotron Plantin
01-9202-57772
Typeset in Great Britain by Centracet, Cambridge
Made and printed in Great Britain

CHAPTER ONE

SARELLA failed to stifle a gasp as the door suddenly flew open. Eyes as dark as night homed in on her own. To her astonishment the intruder kicked the door shut behind him with a thrust of one foot, then proceeded to saunter over to where she was still sprawled in amazement across the bed. Before she could move he dragged the drapes of the four-poster even wider apart and gave her a raking glance.

'How dare you come barging into my room without knocking?' she gasped, scrambling up on to the rumpled counterpane, two hands going up to her blonde hair as she felt his gaze take a rapid inventory of her voluptuous disarray.

'*Your* room?' he rasped, raising dark brows in exaggerated surprise and glancing pointedly at Peter's jacket on the bed.

He turned to look at her, his glance intended to skewer her to the spot, forcing her to clutch self-consciously at the kimono she had slipped on while she had a nap after the arduous car journey into the mountains with Peter just now. His manner made her stammer, 'Haven't you any m-manners?'

His liquid ebony eyes told her it was a pointless question—just as it was pointless to make any attempt at civility. This man of all men wasn't likely to answer to a mere twenty-year-old—and certainly not to one he held in such contempt. She had heard raised voices for the last two hours, ever since she and Peter had arrived, and she was miserably aware that it was all her fault.

5

She swung her long tanned legs over the edge of the bed, forgetting for a moment that she was naked underneath the loosely tied robe, and when she stood up she could feel his eyes trailing insultingly at the V where her naked breasts could be glimpsed. He was a good head taller than she was, and in other circumstances she would have judged him the heart-throb type, with his dramatic dark looks, reckless mouth, strong jaw and a piratical scar across one cheek giving his faultless right profile the touch of humanity it needed. He looked every inch an ex-world-class racing driver. There was courage, ambition, flair, a sense of wildness scarcely controlled— all of this plainly visible in his bearing, and traits Sarella responded to very positively in the abstract. But now, face to face with the possessor of all these qualities, she was aware of the ruthless, hard, uncompromising side to them. It sent her backing nervously towards the casement window as if to set a safer distance between the two of them.

Far below was the cobbled courtyard, the ancient walls of the castle, the drawbridge and the winding road leading back down the narrow valley towards civilisation, but she was trapped in this gaunt grey fortress with this brooding stranger, and she longed only for escape. At the same time she knew escape was out of the question. Defiance made her turn her back, but the sound of a dark laugh sent a chill through her and, jerking her head round, she saw his lips drawn back to reveal a dazzle of predatory teeth. There was less humour than triumph in the sound, and her senses began to swim.

'You could at least have knocked!' She tried not to drop her glance.

'I could,' he agreed with the forbidding smile still on his face. 'But then I'm not used to having to knock on the doors of my own house.'

'*House?*' She gave a bitter laugh. The Castell Rocamar was hardly a house!

'What do you mean?' He inclined his head to study her expression. 'Does it impress you?' He was watching her, the smile gone, but with the same brooding look with which he had entered.

'Impress me? Why should it?' She tossed her head, aware she wasn't fooling him for a minute. But she went on, 'People like you don't impress me with your conspicuous wealth. Sorry to disappoint you.'

'People like me?' He put his head on one side again. 'You know a lot of men like me, do you?'

'I suppose that's meant to be a trick question?' When he didn't reply she added, 'If I say yes you'll think it confirms your view of me as a fortune-hunter. If I say no you'll think I persuaded Peter to marry me as a sort of grab-it-quick opportunity that might not come again!'

'If you say so,' he drawled with a smug expression. He continued to look her up and down, with no evidence of warmth at what he saw but just a tightening of the hard lips and that aloof dark stare she had already witnessed.

'You're completely wrong about me,' she told him quickly. 'I'm not after your brother's money. I didn't even know he had any——'

'Ha!' The dark head rose and fell.

'It's true!' she burst out. 'I hadn't *any* idea! He just seemed like one of us——'

'Us?'

'You know, the gang at the ski-shop. You must know what I mean.' Did he know? She wasn't sure what he knew, but she did know by now that most of what he thought he knew was all supposition. 'It's difficult to work out somebody's background when you only see them on the ski-slopes or fooling around *après-ski*. Not that anybody would interest themselves in that sort of thing anyway—it simply isn't important,' she added rather lamely. She was right, but the way he was looking at her was completely unnerving. He was somehow managing to make her begin to doubt her own words— simply by subjecting her to that look of dark unbelief. Why was he staring like that?

'So when did you find out he was quite wealthy?' he asked casually.

Quite wealthy, Sarella registered with an inward smile. That was the understatement of the century! 'I suppose I really understood what was at stake when I got my first glimpse of the castle,' she admitted, unable to disguise a rather wry smile.

His black brows shot up in disbelief. 'This morning?'

She nodded. Plainly he didn't believe a word she said.

He confirmed this impression by asking in tones rank with disbelief, 'You mean to tell me you thought you were pursuing a poor man?' He gave a cynical laugh. 'I believe in fairy-stories too, my dear.'

'I've never pursued any man in my life!' she flared, stung by his disparaging 'dear' as much as by what he seemed to believe.

'Maybe not,' he agreed coolly, 'at least, not until the right one came along!'

'Peter?' Her lips twisted and she gave a croaking laugh. 'It was entirely the other way round. *He* pursued *me*.'

'And you knew nothing about his family when you finally succumbed to his persuasion?' His voice dripped sarcasm, telling her plainly what he thought of that.

'No, I did not know!' she remonstrated. 'He didn't mention *you* until he asked me to come up here with him.'

'This was, of course, after he asked you to become engaged.' The cold eyes assessed her reaction.

Sarella was silent for a moment. How could she tell this hostile man that his brother had only suggested she pretend to be his fiancée as they'd turned into the long drive leading up to Rocamar? Only his promise to explain fully later on had made her say a grudging yes.

'So,' he continued when she didn't answer, 'he told you about me before you agreed. As I thought.'

'That's not true!' she exclaimed, wanting to step forward and grab him by the arm. She knew it sounded unconvincing and she could read the continued disbelief in his eyes even as she spoke, but it wasn't right, the way he was managing to give a nasty twist to everything she said. It wasn't fair. She really was fond of Peter. He was a darling: good-looking, charming, the sweetest man—boy—alive. Her misgivings about what he was asking her to do had been put to sleep by his open face and little-boy smile. He could get anybody to do anything for him, he was so sweet.

'And, having known him two months,' the prosecution was going on, 'you found out nothing about his background?'

'You don't *understand!* We didn't sit around discussing the past with each other. We just used to banter, have the odd drink together, fool around in the snow. It was winter sports, for heaven's sake, not an in-depth seminar on personal relationships! And anyway, Peter's not like that! You know he doesn't go in for a lot of heavy discussion about things.'

'Yes.' He gave a heavy sigh. 'Unfortunately he's always been lightweight.' So Peter was condemned without trial too. Her prosecutor was looking at her as if she'd just crawled from under a stone. 'I admire your tenacity in sticking to your story,' he intoned, 'but even you can't really expect me to believe a word of it. You insult my intelligence, my dear.'

Sarella wished he would stop calling her his dear. He hated her. Had hated her at sight. At least, he'd hated her after that single flare of interest as she'd climbed out of Peter's hired jeep, but it had died instantly when, striding boyishly round the front of the vehicle, Peter had gone straight up to his elder brother and announced, 'Meet my amazing fiancée, big brother!' And he had turned, his sweet face alive with devilment, one arm outflung as if presenting someone on stage to an audience. Sarella, half in and half out of the jeep, had frozen suddenly as her eyes met those of her host.

'Marc Alexander Vila,' Peter had announced, oblivious to the electricity that had flashed between them. 'Bluebeard to you!' Sarella could have throttled him. Bluebeard had been a private joke—an exclamation she had been unable to stifle as they'd rounded the cliff at the head of the valley and she had got her first glimpse of the imposing turreted Castell Rocamar. At that point she'd had yet to meet its owner. She realised now it wouldn't have changed her opinion one jot.

From that first introduction it had been all-out war.

Now Marc Alexander Vila moved closer, and she found herself surreptitiously pressing back against the stone wall of the turret room she and Peter had been allotted, trying to pretend she didn't care while her breath went ragged with apprehension. The old stone felt cold beneath her fingertips, but it was the glance sweeping over her from out of those black eyes that really froze her senses. She drew in a breath, determined not to be cowed by this hulking brute, but her mouth felt dry as he loomed closer. When he was a pace in front of her, nothing but a jangling space of a few inches between them, his voice was feather-soft.

'You seem to have become engaged in quite a hurry.' There was a pause. 'No doubt,' he suggested, in a voice so soft that she had to tilt her head to catch the words, 'no doubt,' he went on, 'you can disengage with equal speed? I'll give you the money for your flight back to wherever it is you came from——' he might have said 'crawled from', such was the contempt in his voice '—all right?'

Sarella drew herself up. Her knees were trembling. 'You mean you're trying to buy me off?'

He gave her a glance, adding heat to the frigid atmosphere, then, as if deciding against tact, gave a small nod of the black head. 'Quite so.'

She gave a gasp at the insult. 'I see. . . And that's my price, is it? An air ticket?' She raised her own eyebrows.

'You're playing for higher stakes?' His lip curled. She could read the expression in his eyes. It said he'd expected this.

'A-actually,' she managed to stammer as haughtily as she could, 'I'm not playing at all, but you won't believe me.'

'But you'll do as I say and undo this little mistake,' he said swiftly, as if it were a foregone conclusion.

'I don't regard my engagement to Peter as any sort of mistake,' she managed to say. 'And I'm not going to commit myself to anything until I've had a chance to talk to him.' Her fingertips were numb where they were pressing into the stone wall behind her.

'You have faith in your powers of persuasion.' It was a statement of fact, one which again damned her, implying, as it did, that she had been the one to manipulate Peter into a liaison.

She turned to the window, a deliberate shutting out, praying he would go now that he'd had his say. There was something about battling with him that made her feel unlike herself—weak, her mind in total confusion. Although she had nothing to lose but her pride, she

sensed that there was more than that at stake—much
more. What it was she couldn't guess, but his enmity
seemed deeper than it should have been, given that
they'd only just met. It was as if he wanted to destroy
her in some way.

She traced a pattern over the rough-hewn stone of the
sill, while behind her there was no sound of retreating
footsteps. In fact, she sensed him move nearer.

'Where is Peter now?' he demanded from right behind
her.

Sarella jerked her head round, then gave a small gasp.
Marc had indeed moved closer. He was standing right
behind her, so close, she registered, that she was aware
of the subtle body-scent of him, sandalwood, leather.
Her breath caught in her throat. For a moment neither
of them spoke. Her eyes fixed on his lips, drawn to the
wide mouth as if its imprint was but a breath away, then
with an effort she dragged her glance from them, half
turning to avoid the intensity of his regard. 'You're so
wrong about me!' she blurted. 'So prejudiced! You
imagine that whatever you think must be right! You're
the most bigoted man I've ever met. What right do you
have to sit in judgement on somebody you hardly know?'

'You think I would change my opinion if I got to
know you better?' he asked in a voice like velvet.

She was so caught up in her own feelings that she
failed to detect the danger in the question. She nodded
her blonde head. 'Of *course* you'd change your mind
about me if you really knew me——'

'So how, then, do you propose we get to know each
other?' he asked in the same soft tone.

Too late she realised the trap she had stumbled into.
The way he was looking at her now, his eyes an open
invitation to sin, told her plainly he had only one answer
in mind!

Standing right on top of her by now, he was preventing her from walking out unless she actually brought herself to push past him, and she feared the follow-up to their slightest physical contact. She was aware of his body-heat and it was making her head swim. She struggled to keep her mind on facts instead of letting it career off in confusion, but her whole vision seemed to be swimming with his devilishly smiling face as he hovered over her, waiting for her answer.

'I didn't mean we should get to know each other——' She broke off, not sure what she did mean when he looked at her in such open invitation. If she hadn't already had evidence of his contempt for her she would almost be taken in by this new smiling look.

'But maybe that's the answer,' he suggested, his tone thickening. 'Maybe we should take a little time out. . .just the two of us. . .You could show me how persuasive you can be.' He lifted an eyebrow.

'You're confusing me,' she managed to say, rubbing a hand over her eyes. She felt strong fingers catch hold of it, grasping it firmly and pulling it away from her face.

'Don't hide from me,' he murmured, excusing his action yet failing to release her wrist after he'd forced her hand down, his thumb moving over the inside of her wrist as if by accident. 'I like to watch the expressions flitting across your face,' he went on. 'You have a very expressive face. Has Peter told you that?'

She couldn't answer. It felt as if red-hot needles were shooting up her arm. Her flesh burned where he touched it. Inexplicably her body seemed to have a desire of its own—to go on being touched by him.

But he was speaking now, the words dropping like hard pellets into her mind. 'He also told me you were an actress,' he stated. 'That you took a job in the ski-shop at Soldeu because you were "resting", as you people call it when you're out of work——'

'I'm——It's not——What else has he told you?' Sarella failed to gather in her scattering thoughts, but knew that whatever she or Peter had said was being stacked against her, no matter how innocent it really was. She could tell as much from his tone of voice. Now he seemed to be implying that there was something immoral in how she earned her living.

As she opened her lips a little to defend herself he went on, 'Peter hasn't told me much. But what he has told me I found rather interesting—in the circumstances,' he added pointedly, confirming her suspicions.

'Don't worry, I won't get any idea that you're interested in me!' she replied in a weak attempt to say something in her own defence. 'I know anything you discover will only be grist to your mill!' Already her entire body seemed to be turning to fire and ice, and it was all she could do not to let her trembling knees fold, collapsing her at his feet like a rag doll—which was exactly where he probably imagined she should be. His hold on her arm seemed to be doing nothing to him at all. Longing to scream at him to set her free, she reminded herself of her drama-school training, and instead forced herself to look as if she had no more feeling than a block of wood.

His eyes raked her face. 'Grist to my mill? Whatever can you mean?' He went on relentlessly, 'You are an actress, aren't you? He didn't get it wrong, did he? And you were working at the ski-shop in order to keep body and soul together?' His voice remained quiet and reasonable, although what he said flew beyond reason.

'You're twisting the facts, making it seem as if I'm just acting a part! That's horrible!' He was giving a slant to the facts that was difficult to counter, and if she said too much she was afraid of betraying Peter's trust. Her first loyalty was to him—at least until they could have a talk and straighten things out. Poor Peter. What on earth had led him to engineer a situation like this? Marc really seemed to have him on the run. He was a monster! Now his fingers were pressuring over the skin inside her wrist again and she wanted to snatch her hand away, but, as if guessing her intention, he tightened his grip, pulling her a centimetre—no, more—towards him. It was enough to render the distance separating them as nothing. They were virtually in each other's arms. His lips hovered over her forehead. She had to raise her face in order to see what he was going to do next. What she saw in his eyes made her catch her breath.

'When my kid brother turns up with a blonde blue-eyed actress on his arm, and apparently engaged, I'm naturally inclined to think the worst,' he told her, scarcely moving his lips. He was so close, so close. She could see the minute bristles on his jaw, imagined, before she could stop herself, the rough male touch of them over her skin.

Oblivious to these thoughts, he went on, 'You're a very beautiful young woman.' He lowered his head a fraction. 'And Peter's such a boy.' His eyes were hooded.

Sweeping waves of desire were pitching Sarella head-long to the point where she knew she was leaving common sense behind.

That moment in the courtyard when their eyes had met had been real after all! Real for him. Real for her. How could they pretend it hadn't happened?

But just as his lips approached an inner voice ordered her to pull back.

Her eyes dilated as she arched away. 'Don't. . .!' she warned breathlessly. 'Have you forgotten I'm engaged to your brother?'

Marc seemed to freeze in the act of bending his head. 'But I shall be your brother-in-law very shortly, so what's a brotherly kiss?' he murmured. 'You can't object to that.'

'I can and do,' she responded shakily. 'And I'm sure Peter wouldn't approve.'

'But Peter's not here,' he insisted, starting to lower his head again.

'That's not the point,' she objected, flattening herself against the wall. 'He wouldn't like it.'

'You must have worked magic on him—he's always been so generous with his possessions,' he smiled, adding softly, 'as, of course, you must have discovered.'

His voice had hardened a fraction, momentarily out of control, and Sarella thanked her lucky stars for that warning note. He hadn't revised his opinion of her at all! Despite his apparent desire, matching the sudden irrational flaring of her own treacherous libido, he still suspected her of having designs on the family fortune, and she wouldn't be at all surprised to discover that his attempt to kiss her just now had been a sort of test. If she hadn't resisted he would no doubt have made sure Peter knew at once that she wasn't to be trusted!

She wondered how that would have changed the equation. It made her feel sick. From everything being simple and light-hearted, she had been plunged into shoals of deception, way out of her depth. The worst bit was to know that, despite it all, this horrible, devious monster actually turned her on!

She averted her head, blonde hair swinging across to screen her face. Marc was still gripping her wrist in a way that made her feel like melting against him. 'Please,' she whispered, 'you're standing too close.'

'Really? Are you sure you mean that?'

Not daring to look at him, she nodded with head

back, eyes shut. 'I don't know why you're doing this to me,' she said achingly.

When there was no answer she risked a glance. His eyes, pinned to her face, were carefully blank. She couldn't tell whether he felt anything or nothing. He was in total control of his responses, just as he must have been, she registered, when he drove all those winning cars to victory—until the last one, of course.

Lime and leather assailed her nostrils in a tantalising cloud as he bent his head, and before she could object he pressed his lips lightly on her mouth and stepped back. It was intended as a mark of possession—passionless, deliberate. His sign of impending ownership, telling her he would be back.

A deep shuddering breath ran through her, her breasts tightening with the anticipation of what might follow. But through the haze of repulsion and desire she was aware of another sound.

Her limbs froze. Instead of fire there was ice in her veins. She opened her eyes. The bedroom door had burst open and Peter was striding into the room.

In a dream, she saw him skid to a halt, taking in the scene at once as it must have appeared—his brother bending over his fiancée—and, thought Sarella in dismay, taking in my submissive expression as I stupidly allow this dark monster to maul me. Furious with herself for allowing such a situation, she pushed Marc's hand away, panting slightly with suppressed emotion at the misunderstandings she knew must follow.

A look of confusion had flashed across Peter's face, then he gave a short laugh, a more boyish version of his brother's cynical bass, and said, 'So you two are getting to know each other. I thought big brother wouldn't lose any time in making you welcome at Rocamar, Sarella.'

'It's not like that!' she blurted, anxious to set the record straight at once.

But Marc turned and, to Sarella's embarrassment, instead of moving away, placed one hand possessively on the wall beside her head and leaned there, with a smiling glance over his shoulder at his younger brother. 'She's quite delectable, Peter. I didn't suspect you'd developed such good taste!'

'No need to make a meal of her!' Peter tried to sound casual, but Sarella could see he was worried underneath. Had she betrayed him already? he seemed to be asking.

Their eyes met and she dropped her head guiltily before managing to say, 'Don't worry, Peter. It's not the way it looks——' She broke off. If only Marc would go away she could reassure Peter that she wouldn't let him down. If it was a battle between the two brothers she knew whose side she was on!

'Nothing with you is the way it looks—so you would have me believe,' observed Marc with a sardonic downward glance.

'You've certainly changed your tune, anyway,' Peter went on, effecting an indifference to the situation. He gave his brother a puzzled smile. 'I thought you were intent on warning me against her. Now it seems you rather approve my choice.'

Marc, to Sarella's relief, removed his hand from beside her head and strolled over to his brother. 'Don't misunderstand. I haven't changed my tune at all. There are women and women. Only the special few are eligible as wives. That's something you're still too young to appreciate.'

Peter scowled. 'You're too late with your advice— twenty-four hours too late. I've made up my mind. I'm getting married.'

Marc put his hands in his pockets, apparently un-ruffled by Peter's doggedness. 'If you really thought what you were doing was above-board you would have invited Sarella here long before this.'

'Maybe I knew you'd try to stop me. You'd tell me I was too young to get engaged to anyone. You've always told me I'm too young. When I'm eighty you'll still think it! But you'll have to get one thing into your head—I'm going to live my own life and nobody's going to stop me. I'm not a fool. I simply want to enjoy Uncle's money while I'm young enough!'

'Oh, the money! Back to that!' Marc's eyes flashed. 'Have you forgotten I have to give my approval before you lay your hands on a penny of it? Uncle knew what he was doing when he said you'd have to show you were serious about settling down and getting married in order to inherit. But you know as well as I do he meant you to be involved in a serious attempt at marriage. Not this!'

'You read it as you like!' Peter burst out defiantly.

'I shall! I shall!' Marc laughed again with a scathing humour that seemed to cut Peter to the quick, but Marc went on, 'You don't mean you're going to enjoy Uncle's money, you mean you're going to squander it. You want to throw it away on the first blonde blue-eyed gold-digger to throw herself across your path.'

Peter went white, then as the colour returned to his face he put up his fists. 'You can't say such things——'

'Who's going to stop me?' Marc faced him, broad-shouldered, adamant. 'Wise up, damn you,' he growled. 'See her for what she is. You saw her just now and you've been engaged less than twenty-four hours! What sort of life do you imagine you're going to have together? Do you think she'll stay when she's bled you dry?'

'Don't say that!' Peter lashed out at his brother, missed, stumbled and would have fallen if Marc hadn't shot out a hand to stop him. He forced Peter's arms to his sides. 'Don't fight me, Peter. I'm on your side, and I'm only saying this for your own good.'

Peter was almost in tears, and Sarella felt her heart turn over. How on earth could she have guessed she would be the cause of such strife with that casual agreement charmed out of her less than twenty-four hours ago?

'Stop it, both of you!' she exclaimed, pushing herself between the two of them. 'I'll leave if that's what you both want. I'll go right away. I only want what's best. I can't bear to see you behave like this towards each other!' When neither of them made a move she turned to her things on the bed.

Peter reached out for her. 'Don't go. You can't leave me! Please, Sarella. Take no notice of him. He can't do a thing. I'm twenty-one now. I'll do what I want for a change! He always has to interfere. He thinks he owns everybody!' He turned on Marc again. 'I'm not going to fight you—you're not worth it. If she goes, I go. You choose. But I'm not giving her up. I want to enjoy life while I can. And Sarella's going to help me. It's nothing to do with you! So back off, Marc. Let me run my own life!'

'You little fool!' Marc took a step forward as if about to restrain his younger brother by sheer force, but again Sarella stepped between them, hands outstretched, grasping Peter by the arm, though she was careful not to touch so much as the edge of Marc's sleeve.

'Can't we all sit down like sensible human beings and discuss this?' she pleaded. 'Heaven knows, when I agreed to this I'd no idea it would cause such anger——' She gave Peter a reproachful glance.

'You hadn't?' Marc gave a cynical laugh. 'What an optimist!'

'It's *true!*' She turned on him, flinching as fire seemed to ignite between them.

'Well, you might not have, my dear,' he added unfuriatingly, and apparently impervious to the effect he was having, 'though I by no means concede that point. But Peter here certainly knew what he was doing. And if he'd any sense he would have guessed my reaction. The amazing thing is he actually believes he'll get away with it!'

'At least you're not putting the entire blame on me now,' she couldn't help remarking.

Marc gave her a freezing glance. 'I'm not conceding anything. I know your type through and through.'

'You think you do!' she flared, unable to help herself.

Now it was Peter's turn to intervene. 'Let's do as Sarella suggests and sit down calmly and listen to what each of us has to say.'

Marc let his glance laze from one to the other, then his lips quirked in a humourless smile. 'She has got you under her thumb, Peter, old boy. When she speaks, you jump!' He gave his brother a mocking glance, then moved towards the door. 'It's obvious nobody's going anywhere tonight, so we may as well play out the charade of being rational people. I'll expect you both down to dinner at eight.' He looked pointedly at the four-poster bed with its rumpled coverlet, then back at Sarella. 'Don't be late, Peter, will you?' Then he left.

Peter put out a hand and gripped Sarella by the shoulder as she took an involuntary pace forward. 'I'm sorry. I'd no idea he'd take it as badly as this.'

She swivelled so that his hand slid from her shoulder. Her cheeks were flaming after Marc's last gibe. 'How dare he insinuate such a thing?' she hissed. 'Did you see that look? He thinks we're going to make love!'

Peter didn't look too put out by the idea. 'That's what

most normal couples would do, given the chance,' he observed.

She went over to the bed, realising with a shock that she still wore her kimono. She untied then retied the belt with nervous fingers, not quite sure what to do next. When she turned her face was full of concern. 'You must tell me the truth,' she said. 'And tell Marc everything too. You must.'

Peter's first reply was unprintable. He strode over to the window and leaned his head against the glass. 'I don't want to lie to either of you, Sarella, but it's all so difficult right now. I'm not quite sure what I ought to tell you yet. It's just——' He lifted his head and looked straight at her. 'It's just that Uncle was a cautious old devil and——' he looked away '—he got the impression I was a bit of a spendthrift because—well, because I used to get through my allowance pretty rapidly when I was away at school, and. . .oh, hell, he wanted to make sure I was going to be dull and sensible about all that money when he finally kicked the bucket. But, you see, I need it, Sarella!' He took a pace towards her. 'I need it now. I've got to have it!'

When she looked as if she was about to ask him why, he went on, 'There's a good reason—you have to believe it. The trouble is, Marc's taking his role of guardian too seriously. You don't know him yet, but he's as hard as hell. He thinks everybody has the same blind will to succeed as himself. He doesn't excuse mistakes, he simply won't allow them. And he can't imagine weakness. Neither does he know what it is not to be ambitious like him. He's always had this fantastic energy. Nothing can crush him. Not even the accident. Most men would have given up after that. Not Marc. He's always been brilliant. And he expects everybody else to be like that too. He can't understand that people make mistakes.'

His teeth ground into his lower lip. 'Part of me hates him,' he admitted, 'and the other part of me hates *myself* for feeling jealous of such a fantastic guy.'

Sarella went over to him. 'Don't talk like that. It's silly to make yourself feel bad. We're all different. You're so sweet, Peter. You're one of those people everybody adores. We all love you, you know that.' By 'all' she meant the rest of the staff at the shop and the myriad friends he seemed to have wherever he went.

'Love?' He put an arm round her shoulders without lifting his head. 'As Marc said of women, there's love and love.'

'I'm sorry,' she whispered. 'I know when you said "let's pretend to be engaged" you didn't mean it to be for real.' He was sensitive enough to read the confusion in her eyes, and it was obvious he didn't know what to say. She wondered again what sort of trouble he was in and how she could best help.

He turned to face her and they rested their foreheads together like brother and sister. 'I talked you into this. I'm sorry. I shouldn't have. But you're not the love of my life—and I'm not the love of yours. That's why it was easy to ask you to help me—I knew there would be no broken hearts. I want to explain, but somehow I can't; not just yet.' His grip tightened. 'Will you stand by me, Sarella? As a friend? Please, I'm asking you to give me your blind trust and it's unfair of me, but there are things I can't bring myself to confess just yet. So will you trust me? Please. . .say yes.'

CHAPTER TWO

PETER caught hold of Sarella by the arm when they reached the bottom of the stairs, and before they entered the dining-room he pleaded, 'Stand by me, Sarella. Everybody goes over to him. They always have.'

'Not me,' she said loyally. 'No matter what he says.'

He put up a finger and stroked her cheek. 'I think he puts the fear of hell into everybody.'

'I'm not afraid!' She gave a shaky laugh, wanting to add something to the effect that it wasn't fear that drew people to Marc, but more like sheer charisma. Instead of saying so, she pecked him on the cheek. 'Don't worry, love. I don't give in easily to anybody, and together we're invincible!'

He slipped an arm around her waist and gave her an affectionate squeeze. Just then a shadow fell between them.

'Come along, you two love-birds. You have to eat as well, you know.' It was Marc, his voice cutting like a whiplash with unconcealed sarcasm. He pushed ahead of them, and Peter had to hurry forward to stop the door from swinging shut behind him.

'Take no notice,' he whispered. 'This time there's nothing he can do.'

When they went in Marc was standing at the high-arched window at the far end of a long refectory made sepulchral by huge arching beams of dark oak. It was more like a medieval monastery than a home, thought Sarella, but, despite that, there was something rather magnificent about it. She noticed the eight-pointed-compass shape in the stained-glass window, beneath which Marc was standing, that she had observed in mosaic on the floor of the entrance hall. Words were painted along each arm, but she was too far away to be able to make them out.

Peter went over to a carved oak buffet where drinks were laid out, and at the sound of clinking glass Marc said over his shoulder, 'Don't start knocking it back. I don't want a drunken brawl on my hands.'

Sarella sucked in her breath at the injustice of the remark, especially when she noticed the whisky glass in his own hand.

'Peter holds his drink very well,' she said protectively. '*I've* never seen him drunk.'

Marc swivelled, dark brows lowering with dislike. 'I can see why he's eating out of your hand at present,' he said cuttingly. 'Do you really think he needs nursemaiding?'

'You obviously do!' she retorted.

'Oh?' He swung his dark glance towards Peter.

'Treating him as if he's incapable of making up his own mind about anything. He is twenty-one, you know!'

Marc gave a getsure of impatience but didn't say anything, and Peter, a glass of something that looked like a triple Scotch in one hand and Sarella's usual orange juice in the other, moved smoothly forward. 'Cheers!' he said, upending his glass with an air of defiance and swallowing most of its contents in one gulp.

Sarella turned away. She wished Peter had told her more about the situation before getting her involved. The battle between the two of them was nothing to do with her. It was obviously something far more long-standing than her relationship with Peter. She wished they could both make it up and release her from this terrible trap. Marc made her feel soiled. It wasn't fair when she hadn't done anything to deserve it.

Having observed Peter's defiant behaviour with the drink, Marc tightened his lips and said, 'We'll eat now while you're still sober enough to appreciate Pierre's cooking.' He went over to an ornate walk-in fireplace surmounted by heraldic animal heads carved in stone and pulled a fraying red cord. A few seconds later the doors at the far end of the room opened and a man in a white jacket pushed a laden trolley into the room. Sarella tried not to look over-impressed. It was a shock to discover that Peter was so different from the way she had imagined. It had never occurred to her that he came from the sort of background where servants were a matter of course and all one had to do in order to eat was pull a bell.

She sat down next to him, trying not to show her awkwardness. Marc, naturally assuming the head of the table, frowned when he saw where she had placed herself, but said nothing. Too late Sarella noticed the place set on Marc's other side. Nothing, though, would induce her to sit in such close proximity, and she pretended she hadn't seen it until the man in the white jacket swiftly replaced everything in front of her without a word.

When he left Marc gave her a tight smile. 'Little victories. Make the most of them. Now,' he went on before she could reply, 'I suggest we eat first, then discuss matters—if there is anything to discuss—afterwards.'

Peter nodded. She could tell he was relieved to be let off the hook if even for only a few minutes, despite his words as they'd come downstairs.

She squeezed his hand underneath the table and he gave him a darting smile in response. Marc, of course, letting nothing slip his notice, raised one eyebrow the merest fraction, a gesture that spoke volumes. Sarella felt her cheeks begin to burn, as if caught out in some way. All in all it made for an uncomfortable meal, despite the chef's first-class skills, and Sarella at least was pleased when it was all over and Marc, with deliberately precise timing, pushed his chair back to signal that they could now follow him out.

She noticed for the first time that he had a slight limp. It didn't slow him down and he led the way briskly into a comfortable room adjoining the refectory. It was another one of the tower rooms, with a semi-circle of windows giving on to the mountains, and for a moment they all halted on the threshold, too stunned to move by the sight of the magnificent blaze of the setting sun throwing the snow-covered peaks into relief. 'Yes,' breathed Marc, the first to recover, 'always spectacular. You'll surely miss it, Peter?'

He gave his brother a quick glance, then arranged himself in the most comfortable-looking chair in the room. Sarella was conscious that he deliberately declined to offer her a seat. It was yet another instance of how low in his esteem she stood.

Peter, ignoring his brother's gibe about missing the sunsets, went to the window and stood gazing out for a long time without speaking. When he turned it was obvious from his face that he had been having a long tussle with himself.

Hoping he had decided to make a clean sweep and tell Marc everything, Sarella waited to hear what he had to say.

He moved to her side and took her hand, pulling her down on to a sofa facing his brother. She felt as if they were face to face with an inquisitor. On trial. But it was unfair. No one had done anything wrong. Peter had simply got himself into difficulties. She had tried to help him. And now Marc would hear this and relent.

'You've been very unkind to Sarella,' began Peter. 'It isn't the way you imagine. She's been a good friend to me.' He gripped her hand hard. 'It wouldn't be asking too much to apologise to her.' She saw him stick out his lower lip, a quick glance at Marc's expression showed her the folly of such a request.

'It doesn't matter,' she intervened, knowing they would be here all night if Peter insisted on extracting apologies from someone like Marc Alexander Vila. 'I can live with your brother's opinion. What's important is for you two to get matters straight between you——'

Peter shushed her. 'Let me handle this, Sarella.'

With a sinking feeling she knew what he meant—he had no intention of telling his brother how he'd got himself into this situation. And if he didn't do that she couldn't possibly see how they would ever see eye to eye.

Sure enough, Marc quirked his brow and asked, 'You intend to stick to this story that she knew nothing of your financial prospects?'

'Of course she didn't. She's not the least interested.'

'But she knew you owned the ski-shop.'

'Ski-shop!' Peter dismissed what was a thriving little business as if it were a run-down whelk stall. 'You don't imagine a real gold-digger would have consented to marry me to get her hands on *that*, do you?'

'Not at all. That's precisely my point.' Marc smiled benignly from one to the other, the insult making Sarella's cheeks blaze.

Peter dismissed this with a shake of his head. 'Actually, without Sarella the place wouldn't be as successful as it is,' he confessed generously. Sarella secretly agreed with him. Peter wasn't interested in business. He had never made any bones about it, and, to be honest, he was much more use out on the slopes, chatting people up, showing off the exclusive styles they sold and being a general advertisement for the place. That was what was so endearing about him, but she hardly thought it was something she should mention to his brother!

She herself had soon found a niche in the shop, organising the part-time assistants, seeing to the wages, ordering stock, being a sort of general manager. She had had more responsibility that she'd expected, but she had enjoyed it and welcomed the stability it had brought to her erratic life. There was a good, steady wage, and a proper job was more than she had ever hoped for when she'd first noticed the advertisement written in felt-tip in the corner of one of the windows. On a week's package holiday at the time, the first break she had been able to afford since leaving drama school, it had taken her all of five minutes to make up her mind to stay. The job came with a room above the shop. And the skiing was superb. All that had been two months ago. Now it seemed like another life.

Marc was saying, 'When I gave you that place on your twenty-first birthday, Peter, I foolishly imagined it would help you settle down as you seemed to have no idea what you wanted to do with your life. Apart from moving through it as fast as possible on a pair of skis,' he added with an unexpected flash of humour. It was like a door opening suddenly, and for a split second Sarella saw behind it to the affection Marc felt for his feckless younger brother.

It's true—Peter can be infuriating, she registered. And, to someone with Marc's undoubted ambition and sheer grit, he probably seems hopelessly in need of a helping hand. She almost felt sympathy for Marc if he imagined he could change what was deeply ingrained in

Peter's nature. But then she remembered the insults he had piled on her and she stifled any sympathy before it got out of hand.

'I know you'd like to see me become a big tycoon like you,' Peter was saying, 'but you'll just have to face it— I'm not and never will be. Nor am I going to be the world's greatest skier. I'm not ambitious enough to try for the top.'

'You've got the talent,' Marc cut in.

'Yes, but not the drive.'

'You don't *want* the drive—you're scared of failing!' Marc got up, face like a thunder-cloud, the look he gave Peter designed to shrivel him on the spot. Sarella felt his hand tighten on hers and she leaned against him to reassure him. No wonder Peter lacked confidence and spent all his time merely trying to be amusing in the face of Marc's uncompromising thirst for excellence!

Marc swivelled when he came to the window, his black shape outlined against the dying embers of the sun and his face in shadow. But his tone left them in no doubt as to his feelings as he grunted, 'I suggested to your *fiancée*,' he uttered the noun with contempt, 'that she release you from this ridiculous arrangement. No doubt you've both already discussed this and she has persuaded you to go against my wishes?' She saw him lift his head, alert as a hunter for the slightest weakening in his quarry.

'She hasn't mentioned it——' Peter turned to look at her. 'Is that what you were discussing when I barged in?'

'If you can put it that way,' she said acerbically. 'Your brother has an original way of trying to force people to accept his views.' She matched Marc's disparaging tones. 'All that aside,' she said in a softer voice, 'I do think we should discuss his suggestion, Peter. It may be best for you.'

He gave her a reproachful glance. 'You know it wouldn't.' In an undertone he added, 'For God's sake, you know it would be disastrous!'

Marc moved from his position by the window as if aware of missing this exchange, and came to stand over them. 'You'll get rid of her,' he announced fiercely, 'or, so help me, I'll make sure the will is revoked and you'll get nothing!'

'Even you can't go against the wishes of a dead autocrat like Uncle,' replied Peter, 'though it's probably your dearest ambition! Anyway,' he went on, 'I don't know what all the fuss is about. Either you're worried that Sarella will get her hands on the money, or you're worried I will. There's nothing you can do about the latter, and as for the former you'll simply have to stop worrying. I can assure you, there is no danger whatsoever. She won't take a penny, that was our arrangement. Isn't that so, darling?' He squeezed her hand hard.

'Yes,' she said, looking straight at Marc.

'If you'd bothered to listen to me,' Peter went on, 'instead of simply wading in with all those slanderous accusations about her, I'd have told you earlier.' He squeezed her hand again.

'*Arrangement?* You mean she told you she wasn't interested and you believed her? Is that what you call an arrangement? You're as big a fool as I've always suspected——'

'How official do you want it?' Peter exclaimed, suddenly losing his temper.

'What do you mean?' Marc was standing squarely in front of them both, and Sarella felt he could read everything in their faces.

'I'm simply saying that Sarella disclaimed all rights to Uncle's bequest before becoming engaged to me. Do you want it in writing?'

'That would suit me.' Marc nodded. He was smiling, and Sarella could see the unmistakable signs of triumph on his face. He knew as well as any of them that there was no such document.

'I'll show you!' Peter's face was red. 'I've got it— signed, sealed and witnessed by a notary. Will that satisfy you?'

Sarella concealed a gasp. He was blustering, saying the first thing that came into his head. She waited to see what would happen next.

'It would satisfy me,' replied Marc, '*if* I believed you.'

'I'll make you believe me, so I will!'

'I'd need it right here in my hand.' He lifted one palm uppermost and for a moment seemed half swayed, but his scepticism reasserted itself and he gave an aggressive jerk of his head. 'So where is it, this legally binding disclaimer to your fortune? Aren't you going to produce it?' he rasped out.

'You don't need to see it. You can take my word for it.'

Marc threw his head back with a scathing guffaw. 'Good try, but you surely don't think I'll fall for a line like that?'

Peter glowered back at his brother, then slowly got to his feet. 'All right. If that's your attitude I'll go and get it. If I do,' he faltered, 'you're honour-bound to accept this engagement. You have to. I want my inheritance!' His voice rose. 'If you go on standing in the way any longer I'll take you to court.'

'You will?' Marc was clearly undisturbed by threats. He stood like an immovable obstacle in front of his younger brother. 'Produce your bit of paper,' he rapped out, 'and, although I won't go so far as to give your eventual marriage my blessing, at least I'll let it run its natural course. Your inheritance is yours to squander as you will. If you want to ruin yourself, then, as you so rightly say, you're old enough to know what you're doing.' He looked from one to the other, his bleak glance resting briefly on Sarella's upturned face, and then he said, 'I tell you one thing, Peter; when you're down and out and she's left you for richer pickings don't come running to me for a hand-out, because it won't be forthcoming. Is that clear?'

'Completely.'

The two men stared each other out before Peter gave a sudden exclamation halfway between anger and defeat, and started for the door.

'Where are you going now?' demanded Marc.

'I'm going to bed, if you must know! I've had enough of being treated like a child. And, anyway, I need some sleep if I'm going to leave first thing in the morning. Everything's at the apartment in Soldeu.'

'Get back as soon as you can,' Marc snarled. 'I want to see this bit of paper—if it exists. And,' he paused, 'just to make sure you do come back—with proof of Sarella's uninterest in your affairs. . .' a cruel smile began to play around his lips '. . .she,' he said, 'stays here.'

His dark glance passed briefly over her suddenly ashen face, returning to challenge his brother with an arrogant smirk. 'You have no need to look so put-out,' he remarked lightly, taking in both their expressions with satisfaction. 'Surely you can survive a couple of days apart? If you're telling the truth, Peter, you can be back here in no time. And all's well that ends well.' He gave a hard laugh and turned, avoiding Sarella's stricken glance.

She felt herself shrivel inside. Marc was certainly no fool. He was calling Peter's bluff—but she was the pawn.

'And if I won't stay?' she managed to croak, the prospect of being imprisoned in this fortress of suspicion with a man like Marc Alexander Vila filling her with horror.

'Your disappearance, my dear,' he said with a slight bow, 'would speak louder than words.'

'*You*——!' she breathed half to herself. She turned a stricken glance on Peter. He knew he had been crowded into a corner, but it was his own fault.

He bit his lip when he caught her glance. 'Don't worry. I'll leave first thing and, as he says, I'll be back in no time. At least you'll be comfortable here.'

'Of course you can drive down and drive back and be back *soon*,' she fumed later when Marc had released them after prolonging his cat-and-mouse game with his brother for as long as possible, 'but what's the *point* when there is no paper?' She clenched and unclenched her fists. 'Sometimes, Peter, you are so silly. I can almost understand Marc being driven mad by you. You simply don't think. Why, oh, why did you tell him such a dreadful fib?'

'It's not such a fib,' he countered. 'I know you would have signed a civil agreement if you'd thought of it. You would, wouldn't you? I know you don't care a damn about money.' He tried to take her in his arms, but she pulled away.

'You know I would if I'd thought it was going to turn out like this! Heavens, you know I don't want a penny of your inheritance. But you should have told me the truth from the beginning. You just sort of sprang it on me!'

'I just didn't think it mattered. It's only money.'

'Oh, really! You're impossible!' Sarella marched across

to the four-poster, then spun away. 'Now what? What are you going to do?'

'Leave it to me. I have friends.'

'Oh, Peter. . .' she ran a hand over her face '. . .I just want to block this whole day out, but there isn't even anywhere for me to sleep. Couldn't you have somehow fixed it so we had separate rooms?'

'I'll sleep on the couch—don't worry about that.' He put on a sulky expression. 'Why are you being so mean to me?' he demanded, sprawling full-length across the bed, despite his promise to sleep on the couch, and unloosening his tie. 'Everything was so wonderful on the drive down,' he went on. 'I loved your expression when you first caught sight of Rocamar. It always has that effect!'

'What do you mean?'

'I mean it impresses people.' He gave her a sheepish grin. 'I don't broadcast the fact that I live in a castle. People wouldn't be so nice to me if they thought I was so lucky, but it's fun to see their faces when I bring certain special ones back now and then.'

'Special girls, I suppose you mean?'

'Are you jealous?'

'No, just angry. I don't like being deceived any more than Marc does. You've deceived us both.'

But he wasn't listening. 'It was so sweet when you turned to me and said, "I didn't realise you were a prince." And I said, "The crown prince lies in wait." And you said, "You say that as if he's Bluebeard." How right you were! Now you know what I have to put up with.'

'I thought Bluebeard was married rather more often than usual,' she said tartly, something constricting in the region of her heart.

Peter sat up and grinned. 'You can't say that of Marc. He's a confirmed bachelor.'

'He is?' She couldn't imagine why. She grimaced. 'Presumably that's because he has such a low opinion of women.'

Peter chuckled. 'He certainly does not! And they certainly don't have a low opinion of him either!'

The constriction came back. 'I'm sure I don't wish to hear this.' Sarella marched to the adjoining bathroom. She couldn't imagine any woman with an ounce of sense having a single good thing to say about Marc Vila. 'He's a pompous, conceited, self-opinionated bully!' she called through from the bathroom as she began to slip out of her clothes. 'I can't ever remember meeting a more obnoxious specimen in my entire life!'

She unzipped her dress and let it slide to the floor. 'Just because he won a few stupid car races,' she went on, 'he seems to think he rules the world! And who but a megalomaniac would want to live on the set for a Hammer horror movie?'

Her panties followed the dress and then so did her bra. Naked, she switched on the powerful shower-jets, and raised her voice to be heard above them. 'I bet this place is really spooky late at night. I dread the prospect of staying here while you're away.' She gave a bitter laugh. 'I don't know which is worse—being here alone in Bluebeard's castle or being cooped up with Bluebeard himself. . .!'

She was just about to step under the gushing spray when she realised she'd left her sponge-bag in the other room. Stretching out a hand, she felt the water. It was lovely and hot, and she stepped under it, arching under the fast stream, before she could stop herself. The last few hours had been simply hell. Now all she wanted was to wash away the tension.

She arched and twisted with pleasure before calling, 'Peter, be a love and pass me my sponge-bag, would you?'

When she heard him coming through she pulled the shower curtain more firmly shut and stretched her hand round the edge. 'Thanks——' she said, then her lips froze.

She stood transfixed, with one hand out, but her fingers failed to obey the command to take the proffered bag.

It wasn't Peter's boyish hand as expected, but a more mature, altogether more powerful one, with a white cuff and an inch of dark dinner-jacket jutting between the curtains.

With a sudden movement the curtain was wrenched aside. 'Take it, then! This *is* what you wanted, isn't it?'

Sarella gave a gasp as she found herself staring up into the thunderous face of Marc himself. She tried to draw back but there was nowhere to hide. A curtain of water gushed like transparent silk over her naked form, making her skin appear luminous and highlighting every curve beneath his ruthless gaze. Long after he should have turned away out of politeness she could feel his dark glance pricking all over her, sparing nothing.

'Get out!' she managed to croak, bringing up both hands, ineffectually shielding herself from his assault.

'If you'll only take hold of this damn bag so I can go I will. With pleasure,' he ground out. 'But I would like to thank you for one thing——'

'Just get out,' she cried feebly, not knowing where to look and unable to reach for the bag in case she revealed more of her anatomy than she already had.

'One thing,' he said, lips hardly moving. 'I want to thank you for the last five minutes.' His eyes were still trailing indecently all over her, his voice hoarse. 'They must be the only true words either of you have uttered since you turned up here. And, Sarella,' his voice thickened, 'do feel reassured. . .even Bluebeard wouldn't be interested in *you*—at least this one wouldn't—despite the obvious charms of a beautiful body!'

With one final intimate raking of her naked form as if unable to help himself, he allowed the curtain to swish back into place.

Somehow her fingers had automatically closed over the bag he had thrust forward. Now she clutched at it helplessly, scarcely knowing what to do with it. Then with fumbling fingers she extracted her soap and hurled the bag after him across the bathroom floor.

How could he? How dared he? His examination had been a deliberate attempt to humiliate her, and with an audible cry she began to scrub herself all over until she had covered every inch of her body with soap. Only when she had rinsed herself clean and gone through the whole process again did she feel able to step from under the flood of water.

Covered from neck to knee in a thick towelling robe, she swept back into the bedroom a few moments later. 'And what were *you* doing while he was listening to all that?' she exclaimed.

Peter looked up with a sheepish grin. 'I'm sorry—there was nothing I could do. I thought you'd heard me answer his knock on the door as soon as you went in there. Apparently you hadn't.' His smile broadened. 'Still, it's about time he learned a few home truths, don't you think?'

'Not like that! I'd rather have said it all to his face! He made me feel cheap, as if I'm the type to bitch about somebody behind their back.'

'Well, when I've left tomorrow you can tell him what you think to his face to your heart's content.'

He smiled and stretched. 'Sarella, you do look enticing. Can't we share this bed?'

She didn't even bother to reply. How could he even ask? He was nearly as bad as his brother. She felt like running away, but knew it was impossible. She was a prisoner at Rocamar, in this hateful place, with that baleful monster who was only determined to humiliate her. 'I regret ever allowing you to talk me into this crazy scheme!' she exclaimed as she slid into bed and pulled the duvet up to her chin. 'I must have taken leave of my senses!'

'Maybe you were bewitched by the mountains, the music and me!' quipped Peter, oblivious to her genuine anger.

'I feel first and think second, that's my trouble,' she observed. The bewitchment, if any, had evaporated as soon as those black eyes had extinguished that first interested glance and substituted it for one of rampant dislike. Now she felt like crying with rage at her own stupidity. How could she have got herself into a mess like this? She was just too trusting, and, somehow, she had felt so sorry for Peter. He had given her a sob-story and for a few hours—a few fatal hours—she had mistaken compassion for love. The illusion had lasted long enough to make her accept his invitation to spend a few days away as a reward for all her hard work at the shop. She hadn't guessed it would land her in the thick of a family feud. Now she was trapped until maybe tomorrow when tempers had cooled and Peter would tell Marc the truth and Marc would forgive Peter. And she would be free to escape back to her own life and sanity once more.

With that thought, once Peter had left she switched out the bedside lamp and burrowed down. At worst she would be out of here in only a day or two. Back to ordinary life. Despite that reassurance, all she could do was toss and turn all night and run over in her head the insulting things Marc Alexander Vila had said to her.

CHAPTER THREE

SARELLA followed Peter outside into the courtyard as he was leaving next morning. It was still quite early, and banks of mist lay between the mountain peaks, touched by a haze of pink as the sun caught them. There was an other-world stillness about the place, despite the previous night, and even the castle seemed to be touched by magic. It was the setting for a fairy-tale.

The sight of such beauty brought a catch to her throat, and she said, 'Take care, Peter. Just try not to do anything silly—please, for your own sake.' She stood beside him, a doubtful expression on her face.

'Trust me.' He bent to kiss her forehead. 'I know what I'm doing. He can't get the better of me. Remember, we're engaged. It's not too painful, is it? And think what good you're doing by helping me fulfil all Uncle's requirements for getting hold of my inheritance. Marc can't do a thing and he knows it. As soon as I've proved you're not what he thinks he'll have to eat his words. I'm old enough to handle my own money, and he'll have to accept it.'

'It feels wrong,' she muttered. 'You know this wouldn't be what your uncle meant when he wrote his will. He'd expect your engagement to be followed by marriage.'

'Maybe it will be.'

'Not to me.'

'Don't you love me even a little bit?'

'Peter, we both behaved rashly. You know we did. I can't think why. But I'll take some of the blame. I shouldn't have said I'd come up here with you in the first place. It was silly.'

'Does you good to kick up your heels now and then and say "to hell with everything!" Anyway, I'd have been put out if my infallible charm had proved fallible after all!'

'You don't take *anything* seriously!'

'Is that a compliment? I'll take it as such!' When he saw how upset she was he gripped her by both shoulders. 'Don't think badly of me, Sarella. I'm incredibly fond of you. You've behaved like an absolute angel. I'll make it all up to you one day, I promise. Just stand by me for a little bit longer. That's all I ask.' His grip tightened and his evident emotion made her lift up her fingers to his lips.

'I won't let you down. You can trust me. Just hurry back.' She cast a fearful glance over her shoulder. 'I'm keeping my fingers crossed for you.'

He gave her a brief hug, then turned towards the jeep. Just then Marc appeared from the other side of the yard. He was in riding boots and a pair of immaculate white jodhpurs. Sarella found her eyes fastened helplessly to his muscular physique, outlined so precisely by his tight-fitting riding kit.

She dragged her glance away and reached hurriedly up to Peter before he closed the door. 'Don't leave me long, please, Peter!' she whispered.

'You sound desperate,' he chided with a smile of pleasure at the thought that she might miss him. 'Absence makes the heart grow fonder.' He closed the door and leaned out through the open window as he started the engine, but his look was for Marc. 'Be seeing you!' With that, he drummed the engine once, then headed out towards the mountain road.

Sarella turned in time to catch Marc's worried glance

following the reckless path of the jeep, but then he turned, and she could almost believe she'd imagined that fleeting expression when he gave her a cynical smile and said, 'If it's proverbs he wants I could have swopped him a more appropriate one.'

She didn't realise he'd overheard. When she deliberately ignored him he came closer.

'Want to know what it is?'

'Not really.' She was forced to face him as he planted himself right across her path.

'I'll tell you anyway—"When the cat's away, the mice will play."' He burst out laughing, and before she could retort he swivelled and made back towards the stables.

Thinking she was free of him and that it might be possible to keep out of harm's way until Peter returned, she hurried up the steps into the hall. But Marc's business in the stable must have only taken a minute because he was coming in through the great oak doors even before she reached the foot of the stairs.

'What are your plans for this morning?' he demanded, speaking from the other side of the hall.

She turned, one hand on the balustrade. 'I don't really have any,' she faltered.

She was transfixed as he sauntered slowly towards her, conscious that everything had changed now that Peter was gone. There was a raw, exposed feel, an ill-concealed violence in the air. It was as if Marc himself were some sort of electrical power source. Sarella felt her nerves jump and crackle at his approach.

'Of course, I nearly forgot——' his lips twisted when he came to a standstill '—you're newly betrothed. . .' He paused, and she saw his jaw clench as he gave a cynical smile. 'No romantic idyll with your beloved for you. Sorry I've spoilt your expectations. . .' his obsidian eyes darted over her flushed face, framed in its disarray of blonde hair '. . .though maybe,' he paused significantly, 'maybe you'll make do with a temporary substitute?'

There was a long pause, a violence of conflicting emotions at war within her. Her right hand tingled to smack his arrogant face, but she remembered her drama coach's advice, consciously releasing her tension in a long, draining breath; then she said as clearly and cuttingly as she could, 'Whatever has Peter done to deserve a rat like you for a brother? He's the dearest, sweetest boy who——'

'You've got it in one,' Marc cut in with a rough snarl. 'He's a *boy!* I'm sure that's the first thing that registered once you'd assessed his financial potential——'

'Don't *dare* accuse me of wanting him for his money again!' she shouted, suddenly losing control. 'I heard enough from you yesterday!' She put her hands over her ears to shut out a repetition of all those humiliating accusations, her training flying straight out of the window.

He jabbed out both hands and ripped hers from over her ears, pinning them to her sides, grinding, 'We both know you're a little scrubber. Those big blue eyes don't work on me, and, until I see something in writing, a proper, documented civil agreement, nothing you say will convince me you didn't know full well what you were doing. What age are you?' he demanded abruptly.

She was trembling now, partly with rage, yet partly also with the wild mix of hate and desire his touch seemed to arouse, but she forced her trembling lips to function, demanding, '*Age?* What's age got to do with it?'

'If this ever came to court it wouldn't look good for an older woman to be seen enticing a young boy into marriage——'

'You're *mad!*' she exclaimed. 'Older men marry younger women all the time!'

'Custom,' he came back with a satisfied smile. 'Come on, though, how old are you?'

'I'm younger than Peter, actually.'

'You might be telling the truth for once,' he replied insultingly. 'Right now you look about fourteen. A very provocative fourteen——' His voice lowered. She saw one of his hands come up and, putting out one finger, he traced a tingling trail over her lips. She felt them tremble with expectation, parting, a little out of control. His eyes were hooded, attentive to the slightest nuance of response.

'Don't. . .' she managed to breathe. He was playing with her like a predator, judging the point at which she would lose control. She tried to break from his grasp, but as she spoke he released the arm still pinned at her side and placed his hand on the curve of her neck, fondling it in a way that reminded her of an actor she'd once seen playing Henry VIII just before a beheading scene. She shuddered. She would have had to be blind not to see the mixture of desire and destruction in the getsure. 'You hate me, don't you?' Her voice thickened. He hated and desired her, but she couldn't let him know she saw the desire. 'Whatever I say or do, you'll think badly of me. It's not fair. I haven't done anything to deserve it.'

'Don't bleat to me about fairness,' he rasped, his tone suddenly harsh. 'You should have been more careful before you started playing with fire! But you can still opt out.' His grip tightened, his fingers burying themselves in the knot of hair at her nape. 'Though I'm getting the impression,' he continued, beginning to breathe more heavily and increasing the pressure of his fingers, 'that you quite like the heat—despite your ladylike protestations to the contrary. . .'

Sarella felt her body grow hot. Marc didn't miss her response, but gave a confident smile at the accuracy of his remark. She counted to ten as she had been taught when about to deliver a big speech, but when she tried to force some words of outrage from between her teeth her tongue clove to the roof of her mouth and the most she could do was make a small cry of protest deep in her throat. That was just before his lips came crushing down, marauding over her own with all the self-assurance of a pirate king. Yesterday when he had imprinted his lips on her mouth she had had no foretaste of what a deliberate kiss of his could be like. It was strong and irresistible, sending everything swimming out of focus. Her only consciousness was of the pulsing energy washing over her, picking her up, carrying her along whether she willed it or not, his body pulsing against her own with its blatant male need, and she felt helpless against it.

When he decided he had finished he drew back with a reluctant groan, his eyes watchful, devoid of any feeling other than the insatiable one of sexual hunger. Like someone struggling out of a drugged sleep, Sarella flickered open her eyelids, blinking in confusion as if unsure as to where she was. Through the haze of half-closed eyes she could make out his face hovering darkly over her. Her knees were trembling again, but he held her pressed hard against him, both her arms locked behind her back, making it impossible for her to get away.

For a second she imagined that she detected a bleary look within his own eyes—and she knew it must match her own—but then it was gone as fast as summer lightning and she shivered beneath the old familiar expression, that brooding, storm-filled one that she knew boded no good to her.

'Hot,' he judged, releasing her a little. 'Pity I'm too busy. We might have. . .' He broke off and removed his arms from around her waist, and she had to put out one hand to regain her balance.

Rage, in the aftermath of desire, was beating through her skull, but he was already moving away. She watched him turn to one of the inner doors, his head somehow lowered, and when he reached it he looked back with an aggressive jerk of his head. 'Treat the place as your home until he gets back. Of course,' he paused and she thought that was all, but he suddenly added, 'I'll come and find you. . .later.' His eyes, when they met hers, were a smouldering, expressionless black, designed to underline the threat conveyed by his words.

'*Find* me?' Sarella half whispered when he was gone. And then what? He was warning her that he was going to hunt her down. . .and then. . .and then. . .?

Alone, she reached out and clung to the wooden balustrade. Her legs seemed too weak to carry her back upstairs to the sanctuary of her turret room. She was calling herself all the names under the sun, but it made no difference. It was impossible to believe she could have been so stupid as to let Marc kiss her ! What on earth was she doing? Not only did she hate him, it was the exact thing he wanted—a sign that she was the little scrubber he believed she was. Oh, no, no, why did I let him? she groaned inwardly. Yet she knew the answer, and the memory of his kiss burned with the exquisite mixture of pleasure and pain, wrenching her soul from its customary place, changing all things, so that her glance seemed to rest on a changed universe.

Forcing herself to climb the stairs, she eventually regained the turret room. She was breathless, shivering with cold as she hid herself behind the curtains of the four-poster.

What craziness had led her to agree to Peter's plan in the first place? she asked herself, and what now. . .? After Marc, she meant, now what?

I hate that man, she told herself vigorously when she eventually forced herself to sit down and jigsaw the jumbled fragments of her emotions into place. He's not to be trusted. He's cynical. Hard. Cruel. Full of a strange kind of vengeance. He'll use every trick in the book to get what he wants. And what he wants is me—out, she forced herself to add. And all because he's determined to crush whatever spirit of independence Peter has.

She gazed clear-eyed at the mountains outside the window. It was no good hiding the truth from herself. Marc wanted her out, yes. But he also wanted her. She didn't have a lot of experience, but she knew when a man was aroused and when he wasn't. Marc Alexander Vila was as turned on by her as she was by him.

Shuddering at the thought, she forced herself to consider the options. It's impossible! she exclaimed to herself, getting up and leaning on the rough stone windowsill. I've never felt like this before about anyone. I didn't know such strength of feeling existed. I can't think straight. I feel numb to anything but thoughts of Marc. My whole body seems to be on fire. What can I do? I must get away. I must! I must!

But she had promised Peter to stay. She had given her word. It would only be another twenty-four hours until he got back from Soldeu. Surely she could keep her emotions under control until then? Of course she could, she told herself, clenching her fists and gazing unseeingly at the distant mountain-tops. Marc was an experienced and cynical seducer, exactly the sort of man she had always avoided and despised. The theatre was littered with them—and their victims. But she could handle it. She must. Twenty-four hours was nothing.

She hid in her room until nearly eleven o'clock; then there was a knock on the door. Fearing to open it, she nevertheless forced herself across the room, but when it swung open a maid in a black dress and smart white apron stood before her. 'May I do your room, miss?' she asked.

Sarella gave a guilty start. 'Yes—yes, of course.' Leaving the girl to it, she made her way downstairs. Marc had invited her to treat the place like home—she smiled wryly at the thought—but if that was too much to expect she could at least explore. Surely the place was big enough for the two of them?

She set off towards what she imagined was the outer door, intending to walk in the open, but in a moment she had somehow lost herself in the maze of corridors. They stretched on and on, one opening out into another round every corner. Polished parquet and a narrow scarlet runner made them all look the same. Only the view, visible at intervals through the slit windows of the castle walls, was different. She was able to get her bearings this way and soon found herself at the back of the house. The view here gave on to a terraced garden within the walls. A pool, still empty, was filled with last year's yellowing leaves from a nearby orange tree. The skeletons of climbing roses, not yet in bud, trailed in a regimented way against a wall. All the geraniums in their pots had been cut back. There would be a door leading out into this scene. All she had to do was find it.

She was unaware that anyone had approached until she felt a touch on one of the vertebra of her spine. She spun with a cry, already shivering as she saw who it was. Marc let his hand drop to his side. His black eyes bored into hers. There was a strange brightness in them, but when he spoke his voice was expressionless, like that of a man asserting control over himself by sheer force of will.

'I didn't mean to startle you, Sarella. What are you doing up here?'

'I was looking at the garden,' she said, drawing in a sharp breath, adding to herself, and dreaming of escape.

'Not at its best at this time of year.' He was gazing at her, not at the garden, as he spoke, his eyes still bright, hard as diamonds. 'Come down and have a cup of coffee. Did you breakfast with Peter?'

'Yes,' she breathed, her desire to keep him at arm's length dwindling to nothing.

'In bed?' he asked softly, catching her off guard.

'No,' she gasped. 'In the kitchen, actually.'

'Ah.' He gave her a knowing glance, then went on conversationally, 'Old habits die hard. He loves chatting to the staff.'

'And you don't?' She eyed him critically, forcing herself to ignore the pounding of her heart.

'Not in quite the same way.' He gave her a distant smile as if thinking of something else.

She gave a cool glance in return, cautiously pleased that so far she had betrayed nothing of her reaction at standing so close to him. She could control her feelings after all, she told herself. The knowledge made her reckless. 'You're very different people,' she heard herself remark.

'Not surprisingly, as we have different mothers,' he came back, eyes fixed on her lips.

'You're half-brothers?' she couldn't keep the surprise out of her voice. This was something else Peter hadn't told her.

'That's the logical deduction,' he replied with an

infuriating smile. He seemed quite determined to keep her imprisoned against the wall again, and she longed to understand what thoughts were surging through his mind. Strange, conflicting ones, by the look of it.

She shrugged. None of it was anything to do with her. But he seemed to want to explain something. 'My father was an industrialist,' he told her. 'He swopped my mother for a younger woman when he was in his late sixties. Now they're all gone. Peter was rather doted on in his childhood—with the sort of results you see now.'

'He's a very sweet man——'

'Boy, you said before. You said he was a sweet boy. Has he suddenly risen in status?'

'By comparison, perhaps.'

Marc raised two dark brows. 'Really? I must be losing my touch.' Before she could break away one arm had snaked round her shoulders, pulling her towards him and crushing her face against his chest, then his dark head was obliterating the light, his hot lips seeking hers and to her shame finding them without any difficulty. There was a long moment when she strove to clutch on to her dwindling resistance, then something seemed to make it snap, and she gave herself up to the delicious agony of his touch, helpless in his smouldering embrace. When they broke apart they were both breathing heavily. Sarella tried to spin from his grasp, and he let her go as if surprised to see her move so quickly.

After a moment he came after her, one arm outstretched in pursuit. 'Wait!' he called.

She retreated to the other side of the corridor. 'I thought you'd proved your point,' she panted, watching him in rising panic as he moved towards her. 'I'm a scrubber, right? That means you can treat me like this. All right, Mr Vila. I can see there's no point in arguing

with you. Now that you've proved it beyond doubt, *just
leave me alone!'*

'Sarella, wait!' He grabbed her arm as she tried to run
past him, but she shook it off and spun in the opposite
direction. She reached the end of the corridor, but he
seemed to have given up the chase already. She slowed
to a walk. When she threw a look over her shoulder,
however, he hadn't given up at all, but was prowling
towards her with a bemused smile on his face.

Without waiting to find out what it meant, she broke
into a trot and hurried on round the next corner. Then
she knew why he was taking his time. It was a dead end.
She spun round as he strolled into view behind her.

He spread both his arms wide. 'Are you going to put
that in writing too?' he drawled.

'What?' She blinked then got his drift. 'You——'

His laugh cut through her recriminations. There was
a hint of impatience in it. 'Look, let's establish some
ground rules, shall we?'

'I'd like nothing better,' she whipped back. 'One rule
only: don't touch!'

He was blocking her exit now and was enjoying the
fact that she knew it. He shook his head. 'Rule one,' he
said as if she hadn't spoken, 'stop trying to pretend
you're Miss Virgin Snow. Rule two, stop pretending you
got engaged to my kid brother for anything but his
money. Rule three. . .' he paused '. . .make up your
mind whether you want me or not. I'm too old for kiss
and catch.'

Sarella looked at him with defiant eyes. 'I reject all
your rules,' she said. 'They're not even negotiable. As
for wanting you—you must be mad!'

'Are you denying it?' He looked amused.

She decided to brazen it out. 'Emphatically,' she
whipped back.

'So if that's how you respond when you don't want a man—heaven help him you do want!' He was laughing agreeably now, in complete control, but she knew it was a pose, that underneath there was something dark and dangerous which he wouldn't reveal just yet. He said mock-lightly, 'I'll have to get you to change your mind.'

'You'll never do that!'

'No? So is it going to be war?'

'Isn't that what you've wanted from the start?'

His jaw clenched before he could stop it. 'We're not discussing what *I* want.' He moved closer. 'But maybe we should do just that——'

'*Don't touch me!*'

'I don't intend to.' His mouth hardened. 'What I *do* intend is for you to drive down town with me right now, come into the notary's office and sign away any rights you imagine you might have. I'll then drive you to the airport and put you safely on a plane to a destination of your choice. Together with a little something for out-of-pocket expenses. How about that?'

Sarella felt a wave of nausea sweep over her. Only she knew how deeply she longed to escape. 'What about Peter?' she whispered. 'When he comes back and find I'm not here. . .'

She didn't hear what Marc said to her because she was already hearing in her mind Peter's cry of betrayal. He was counting on her. He had partly explained why he needed her help, how it involved complying with the terms of his uncle's will, although he hadn't admitted yet why he needed the money so desperately. What else he had failed to tell her was that there was a fortune at stake—and that the custodian of it was this Bluebeard, this marauding monster. . .who, even now, while she was going through the motions of hating him, was turning her body to liquid honey.

He had forced her back against a closed door, literally and metaphorically. If she opened it and stepped over the threshold—— No; she feared to discover what lay beyond. It was simply too frightening.

She put up a hand and tried to push him aside. He clasped her fingers and brought them to his lips. They were soft, warm, infinitely desirable. She tried to short-circuit the impact on her senses, but there was a blow like a mule-kick to her stomach and she gave an involuntary gasp.

'What game are you playing now?' Marc demanded savagely, dragging her chin up so that he could analyse her reaction. She swayed, and the colour felt as if it was draining from her face. 'What's that look designed to tell me, Sarella? Are you acting?'

He pressed his thumb in the hollow of one of her cheeks and circled it, rubbing it abrasively over her trembling lips. 'You're a damn good actress. I'm impressed. You get every little nuance right, every response, every tiny movement like desire. Blue eyes widening the smallest fraction as if to imply. . . *Damn you*, don't use your wiles on *me*. I'm not susceptible. Understand? You should be on the stage right now. In the spotlight.'

He was staring at her so intently that she wanted to cry out. He was stripping her, forcing every secret emotion into the blaze of light. What did he want with her? Why was he hounding her like this?

He rasped, 'Aren't you longing to get back to the bright lights?'

Shaken by the intensity of the way he was behaving, her lips almost numb with deprivation as he slid his hand into her hair, Sarella could only shake her head, no words possible.

'What's gone wrong?' he insisted. 'You're still at the

beginning of your career. Or is that all a blind?' He gave a harsh laugh. 'Of course it is—what a fool I am not to get it till now. . .You don't have to explain! It's obvious, isn't it? You imagined you'd found a less arduous way of earning a living than trailing round from one audition to the next. Hence Peter. Rocamar. Or, more lucrative still—me!'

Too stunned to speak, she could only stare up at him, and when she didn't defend herself he went on, 'Come down to earth. It's not as easy as it looks, marrying into a fortune. You can be sure that whenever you see the crock of gold there'll be some ogre standing guard over it. Face it. Grow up. In this world you get nothing for nothing.' His eyes narrowed to two small pinpricks of black. 'Maybe I'll make things worthwhile for you—if you make them worthwhile for me.'

At first she didn't know what he meant. 'Worthwhile?' Her eyes opened in bewilderment. Did he mean he could get her a part in a play or something?

'I mean,' he spelled out for her, 'I won't force your engagement to my brother to an end if I feel some aspects of it are going to be—how shall we say?—under my control.'

When she still looked bewildered he said more harshly, 'I'll take the heat off if you'll show some appreciation.'

'You mean——?' Even now his words hadn't sunk in completely.

'Stop fighting me. Admit you want more than a mere boy can offer. You're a woman, Sarella, full-blooded, ripe. . .' his voice dropped an interval '. . .ready for love. . .' His eyes were unnaturally bright. 'Whatever you and Peter were up to last night,' he went on savagely, 'it wasn't enough to satisfy you. Be honest about that at least——' His fingers were biting into her wrists, but she was scarcely aware of the pain as his meaning burst in with hideous clarity.

'No,' she managed to croak. 'How dare you suggest such a thing? I—please don't. . .!' He seemed to be drawing her willing body towards his again, but this time she remembered her vow to resist him. She brought up both her fists and pummelled him on the chest. His reaction was to allow a harsh laugh to escape him, until she struck him hard on the jaw; then his laughter changed in a flash and he grabbed hold of first one fist, then two, holding them easily in one hand while be brought up his free hand and cupped her chin in it.

'Stop it!' she hissed as she felt him begin to pull her towards him. 'I hate you! You're despicable!'

Ignoring her protests, Marc pulled her hips hard against him, moulding her beneath the palms of his hands and forcing her against the silk-covered wall of the corridor.

'Don't fight me. . . You want me. And I want those lips of yours again. . .your mouth. . .' His words, muffled in her hair, showed he was determined to ignore her objections. She found it only made things worse if she struggled, bringing her even more intimately against his muscular shape. She forced herself to keep as still as she could, allowing her limbs to slacken, so that he wouldn't get the wrong idea. Unfortunately he took her lack of fight as a sudden sign of submission.

'That's better,' he murmured against the side of her head. He lowered his own head again, allowing his lips to pressure gently over her face, seeking their pleasure over the rise and fall of her face and neck. Refusing to shut her eyes in case she succumbed again, Sarella fixed her gaze on a point over his shoulder on the scarlet wall opposite. He pretended not to notice and finished by pressing his lips against hers, forcing her teeth open with the tip of his tongue, then exploring her mouth with every sign of pleasure.

It was all she could do not to respond. Pushed to the limit of her self-control, she would have eventually surrendered if he had gone on any longer. But he released her and said, 'Not very responsive. I'm sure you can do better than that when you try.' His eyes seemed to draw in the light like two unreflecting pools and she was unable to tell whether she had dented his ego or not, but the patronising note that came into his voice hinted that she had somehow won that round. He stepped back. 'Come along like a sensible girl and have a nice cup of coffee in the sitting-room, where we can talk.'

'Anything would be preferable to the ordeal of the last five minutes,' she managed to croak.

Marc's eyebrows rose at this, but his face was kept carefully blank. 'Come along, then.' As if the kiss he had forced from her had been forgotten, he released her and swivelled, abruptly leaving her so that she had to follow like a servant at his heels.

It took a moment or two to realise he had freed her from what had seemed the inevitable consequences, but she was still suspicious as, with wildly beating heart, she traced his steps back along the maze of corridors, back to the relative safety of the main hall.

'Later,' he said as he turned with his hand on the door into one of the sitting-rooms, 'I shall want a straight answer to my question. It's a proposition—a business proposition. I don't know why you have such an unreasonable reaction to it. Obviously I don't want a wife of Peter's around the place if she's not going to behave in a civil manner to me.'

'Civil manner?' asked Sarella blankly, wondering if she had actually imagined the last few overheated moments.

'And now you might ask how civil is civil?' With raised eyebrows and the adoption of that cool, emotionless glance he had bestowed on her before, Marc allowed himself a brief, telling scrutiny of her face, then, apparently satisfied with what he read in it, pushed open the door and led the way inside.

CHAPTER FOUR

'SIT down,' Marc told Sarella curtly when the maid had gone out after depositing a tray on a table between them. 'Cream? Sugar?'

She shook her head. 'Can't we get to the point? What do you want to say?' Her hands were shaking as she leaned forward to lift the cup to her mouth, but he mustn't see that, and she replaced it quickly before she spilled a drop.

He shrugged, picked up his own cup and saucer and leaned back in the chair with them balanced on the arm. 'It's not going to work, is it?'

Her glance searched his face for some clue as to what he meant, and when he failed to enlighten her she asked, 'This relationship, you mean?'

He had momentarily closed his eyes, but now they snapped open. 'Yes, with Peter.' He lifted his dark head and gave her a penetrating stare, noted her expression, and asked swiftly, 'What relationship did you think I meant?'

She bent her head so he couldn't see her blush at the thought that he meant their own relationship, and pretended to do something to the heel of her shoe. He waited until this pantomime was over, then asked again, 'What relationship did you think I meant, Sarella?' He knew full well what she'd thought!

Raising her head, she replied, 'Our relationship, of course.' Then, as he drew his brows together in mock-astonishment, she carefully deflated him by adding, 'The relationship of a future brother and sister-in-law. What else?' Seeing she had briefly outflanked him, she pressed her advantage. 'It's not on at all for a brother-in-law to treat me the way you treat me. I know you feel you're justified, that I'm little better than a fortune-hunter. But that can't alter facts. Fact one is that I'm your half-brother's *fiancée*.' She stressed the word to show how important she felt it to be, and went on, 'Fact two is that, whether you like it or not, my loyalty lies with Peter——'

Marc's bark of disbelief didn't make her pause.

'—and fact three,' she continued, 'is that, whatever you say or do, Peter and I are engaged and will remain engaged until we decide otherwise.' That much was absolutely true.

'So you've already discussed my suggestion?' he came back at once.

He was so quick that she was put off her stride for a moment. 'Your suggestion?' she faltered.

'Of breaking it off?'

'Not exactly,' she answered at last with as much honesty as she could without giving anything away. 'But one does talk, and I know Peter well enough to guess that he wouldn't keep me against my will, just as I wouldn't want to keep him. Not surprisingly I'm having second thoughts——'

'Despite the fact that you agreed to it little more than twenty-four hours ago?'

She smiled. 'Sometimes people do things they don't mean. What do they say? Young and foolish? Surely if you think back into your own past——?'

'When I was young and foolish?' he stressed the last word with an ironic twitch of his lips.

She nodded. He knew she was getting at him—imagine a man like Marc Vila admitting to being foolish ever!—but if she kept calm like this she could undermine him just as he had tried to undermine her. This time she was going to get it right.

'It's true,' he agreed after a careful pause, eyes never leaving her face, 'fools never think of the future. I dare say even I've done one or two rash things in my dim and distant youth.' He seemed to regard its remoteness with equanimity, contrary to what she'd hoped. 'Some things, though, have to be taken seriously,' he went on, allowing a faint note of patronage to insinuate itself into his words. 'Relationships, for one,' he went on. 'Promises for another. Some people regard them as throw-away as yesterday's newspapers.'

At this Sarella raised her own eyebrows. 'I can assure you that mine aren't.'

'You had me fooled ten minutes ago,' he stated with deadly calm.

'You attacked me,' she came back as coolly as she could. 'You know you did. I didn't stand a chance.'

He jerked forward as if physically attacked ready to defend himself. '*I* attacked *you*?'

She nodded.

'I can imagine you could stand up in court and say a thing like that without blinking an eye,' he said as if the thought astonished him.

'Of course I could. It is true, after all.'

'You're lying through your teeth,' he ground out. 'You wanted me. You were mad for——' He broke off. 'However, that's beside the point. As I said just now, it's not going to work. You'll never marry Peter. There's something you don't know.' He paused. 'You think you're going to marry a rich man, but you're not. You've made a serious miscalculation. As soon as you realise that, I suspect you'll be off like a shot. I don't know what line Peter gave you, but if he told you far-fetched stories about his inheritance he omitted one thing. You already know what that is——'

'The ogre guarding the crock of gold?' Sarella raised her eyebrows again.

'Quite,' he agreed acidly, his composure completely regained. 'So you see, my dear, you really are wasting your time. I shall certainly stop him inheriting until he's learned some sense. However,' he went on before she could repeat her indifference to Peter's wealth, 'I have it in my power to ensure that the trustees make Peter a rather generous annual allowance. If you really want to be part of our ménage you'll have to accept that.'

'Ménage?'

'You know Peter lives here. He pops down to the shop every now and then to make sure things are ticking over.'

So this was where Peter used to disappear to? She'd assumed he spent time over the border in France, where she knew he had friends. Until he had suggested getting engaged she'd assumed one of the 'friends' was in fact a girlfriend. They hadn't really talked about it. Up until yesterday, when the whole thing had taken shape and he had whisked her away to Rocamar, she had simply been his confidante—at least, that was how she had seen herself, and she'd assumed that was how he saw her too. But she frowned now, for how well did she really know him after all? Suddenly she felt out of her depth as new misgivings began to surface.

'You're looking very thoughtful,' Marc observed sharply.

'We're back to that word "civil" again,' she remarked. 'How civil is civil? I draw the line at being part of a *ménage à trois*.' She bit her lip, searching for firm ground in the morass that seemed to be opening up at her feet. Twenty-four hours, then Peter would be back. The truth would be told. Her fears would be allayed. And then she would tell Peter firmly but gently that it was all off. She had misunderstood his motives and her own. And there was no future for them.

Marc was laughing with soft menace. 'Civil enough to supply a few of the home comforts my bachelor status denies me, perhaps?' He was watching her closely from beneath his brows, his dark face inscrutable.

Her voice had thickened by the time she managed to reply. 'You know the answer's no. It's a waste of time asking me.' Hot rage enveloped her, bringing with it a near-paralysis. If she let her control slip now she would do something violent to him!

'Would Peter really mind?' he went on, oblivious to all this. 'Or has he become possessive now he's come of age?'

'That's nothing to do with it,' she replied chokily, barely able to contain her anger. 'My wishes are what matter too.' You loathsome, despicable man! she was thinking. How dare you insult me like this?

'And you don't wish it?' he went on relentlessly. His dark eyes picked their way with humiliating slowness over every visible inch of her, from the top of her head to the tips of her toes. It was a burning, raking scrutiny, designed to make her aware of his pulsing desire to slake his sexual hunger with her that only needed her nod to unleash itself. It reminded her how he had given her naked body that same assessment in the shower last night.

Inside she was aflood with seas of flame. Rage and a treacherous susceptibility battled equally for control. It felt as if he could see right inside her head so that he knew beyond doubt the minutest detail of her response. A look at her burning cheeks could only prove her reciprocated desire. The whole room seemed flooded with scarlet.

'So you see,' he wound up after an interminable pause in which the flames seemed to swirl between them, 'it's not going to work at all. I would find it too distracting to have you around the place, knowing you felt the way you evidently do about me. . .that is,' his tone changed, 'how much you abhor my touch.' He smiled, on, off. Ice. It was a challenge. Everything about him, from the sleek black head to the jutting strength of his jawline, to the broad, strong, self-satisfied bulk of him at ease in the chair, announced that he knew in the fibre of his being that his touch was anything but abhorrent to her. His self-confidence almost swept her off her guard, but the narrowed black eyes were a warning, and she gave him a small, would-be pitying smile.

'Feelings can't be helped,' she told him; 'they're beyond our control. Perhaps in other circumstances, before Peter, I might have found you attractive enough to——' She checked herself before she got in too deep. 'Be that as it may,' she hurried on, 'I wouldn't feel at home here, beautiful though it is,' she admitted in strangled tones. 'We never intended to live here.' They hadn't got as far as stating any intention on that subject—for the simple reason that marriage hadn't been part of the plan. It had been too far in the future for either of them to contemplate during the whirlwind few hours that had led to their arrival.

'You'd planned to buy somewhere, had you? Or were you thinking of living above the shop?'

Sarella noticed that he put it all in the past tense. 'I told you, we haven't talked about it.'

'Then I suggest you do—and quickly. It may put a different complexion on things. After all, I can't see a girl like you giving up her freedom to live in a squalid little room above a shop—and, believe me, without help Peter certainly can't afford anything else.'

'Then it'll have to be the room above the shop. I shan't mind.' Let him think they were going to get married if he wanted to. Peter would put him straight as soon as he got back.

'Peter will certainly mind,' he said.

She gave him a quick glance. 'Will he?'

He leaned back in his chair. 'You don't imagine I'm going to allow him to come and go here as if it's his own home, do you?'

'I've no idea what you allow or forbid. You're a law unto yourself, aren't you?'

'Yes,' he agreed smugly. 'I suppose I am. I like it that way.'

'Pity everyone doesn't see it in the same light.'

'Oh, they usually do if I give them time.'

She blinked. 'I see,' she said at last, shaping the words with difficulty. Time? She heaved a sigh of relief. That was the one thing he wasn't going to have. She didn't doubt he could be very persuasive—given time. She tried to think herself back into the part of Peter's fiancée. 'Have I got this right? You want to persuade the trustees to withhold Peter's rightful inheritance, and as well as that you'll throw him out of his home too. All that rather than allow him to marry me? You should tell him this. Why tell me?'

'Because, my dear,' Marc gave a perceptible sigh, 'as I've already suggested, if you're not going to play it my way you can best show your regard for him by taking up my alternative offer of an airline ticket before he returns. It would be a clean break. Best all round.'

'And, if I don't, out goes Peter from the ancestral home without a penny in his pocket.' Sarella closed her eyes. It was back to the same old theme. But she had to play along. She couldn't desert Peter yet, couldn't betray him. She no longer knew what he was supposed to be up to. She didn't know anything. Only one thing was clear: she mustn't hurt dear Peter. He had begged her not to leave just yet. All she had to do was stick it out until his return. Still with her eyes shut, she said, 'I'm not leaving before Peter comes back.'

If he failed to come up with explanations to put everything right then, and then only, would he have to face the consequences himself, for it was clear now that she would have to leave—disengage herself from him, as Marc had so succinctly put it—but she had given her word and she would wait until the whole matter could be discussed openly. She had to try not to become confused by what Marc was suggesting—that he wouldn't stand in Peter's way if she herself was co-operative. It was unbelievable that he could suggest such a thing—and she wondered if it was a test of some sort. But it didn't matter. Although he didn't yet know it, he had won hands down. She would leave at the first opportunity, and never again would she listen to the reckless promptings of her heart.

She opened her eyes and darted a glance at Marc, sure by now that he was already planning some further strategy by which to entangle her.

Instead he gave an exaggerated sigh. 'You really are a most stubborn young woman.'

'And you're a most stubborn man,' she countered.

'Stalemate?' His eyes glinted through the black lashes and for a moment he seemed to be offering some sort of olive branch.

'It looks like it.' Until Peter gets back, she added silently.

Marc smiled. When he smiled, and she had noticed before, his face lit up. It wasn't an ordinary smile; it was a thousand-watt dazzle. He could look utterly devastating when he wanted to. The trouble was, whenever Sarella was around he didn't seem to want to.

'What's the matter?' he asked sharply, noticing her expression.

'N-nothing,' she stammered. 'I was just wondering how we were going to get through the next few hours.'

He replaced his white china cup on the tray. 'We will.' He got up. 'For the moment I go to my office, and you——?' He put his head on one side. 'I have never managed to work out what it is unemployed women do during the day——' he gave a neutral laugh '—except between five and seven, of course.' He went towards the door. 'Looking at your face, I gather that's out of the question?' He tilted his head as he paused at the door. His control was superb. She imagined him in his racing days driving at incredible speed towards some treacherous bend with just that same ice-cold look of control on his face. Calculating the odds. She dashed the image away.

'I hope you're not going to be too bored——' he stopped, hand on the door '—though perhaps I could drive you away by boredom?'

'I don't get bored. There's always something to think about.'

He switched on the smile again. 'I expect you have plenty to think about right now.' Then, as he opened the door, he stopped. 'Do you ride?'

She nodded. 'A little.'

'Then take out one of the horses. But get my lad to advise you. See you later.' With a brief nod and a smile that again dazzled and at the same time almost lulled her into thinking things were going to be normal between them from now on, he left.

After he'd gone Sarella sat still for a few moments with her head resting on the chair-back. Marc made her feel as if she'd just had a battle with a steamroller—but she was mildly pleased with herself. She hadn't conceded anything, even though she'd wanted to, and she'd shown him she could be just as determined as he was himself.

A glance at her watch showed her it was nearly midday. Peter would be at Soldeu by now. She thought of ringing him on the off chance of catching him at the flat, but shelved the possibility as unlikely. The shop was closed as the season was virtually over by now, and, although she didn't know what plan he had up his sleeve, she didn't expect him to do more than breeze in and out. She assumed that, having had time to think things over, he was going to come back with the decision to tell Marc everything that had led up to this crazy engagement of theirs. There were a million questions she wanted answering herself.

She managed the next few hours without any problems— Marc seemed to be busy. At any rate, he was out of sight, though not exactly out of mind, and she seemed to have the castle to herself, apart from the distant, discreet presence of the staff. Lunch was taken on the terrace alone beneath the warming rays of the April sunshine, and after that she continued her exploration of the house, amazed at the number of rooms that were apparently shut up and wondering why it was that a man like Marc Alexander Vila would choose to live alone in this enormous and obviously expensive mausoleum.

He was a strange man, she acknowledged. One with all the attributes of a jet-setter, considering the sort of life he must have led before the accident that had put him out of motor racing, yet he seemed to be living here like a monk. Or was that a false impression, created by the odd circumstances of their unexpected arrival here?

Perhaps he'd simply cancelled whatever social engagements he had when he'd realised that his brother needed sorting out?

Unable to answer such questions, Sarella wandered round the library, inspected the books, the collection of videos, Marc's taste in music. Even after giving all the titles a thorough scrutiny she still had no idea what he was really like. He seemed to cater for all tastes in his selections. It suggested that he entertained a wide range of people. There was everything any guest could want.

Feeling surprised that she was no nearer solving the enigma of Mark Vila, she tried to find something to take her mind off things, toying with the idea of running a couple of black and white Marlene Dietrich movies, but a glance at her watch told her that it was already late in the afternoon.

She wondered why Peter hadn't called. He must be on his way back by now. She couldn't wait to see him. Funny. . .she had never expected to feel like this. But she knew it wasn't an increase in affection—it was simply that he represented safety. If Marc was the ogre guarding the crock of gold, then Peter had to be cast as the white knight, saving her from the dreaded dragon!

Forcing herself to be patient, she took down a leather-bound copy of Grimms' Fairy Tales and opened the pages. It was no good, though; she couldn't settle. After five minutes of staring at a woodblock of a hero, who looked remarkably like Marc himself, chopping his way through the briar thicket towards the sleeping princess, Sarella slipped the book back in its place and continued her explorations.

At ground-floor level she discovered a games-room, a large slate-bed billiard table taking up much of the space, and a selection of tennis racquets and other games equipment suggesting that there were the courts and space for all these things. Then she remembered Marc's suggestion that she take a horse out.

She went over to the games-room window. It was raining. Strange how the day had changed, clouds darkening to the west, obliterating the sun. There would be no spectacular sunset this evening, she noted.

There was a small room adjoining the games-room, and she poked her head round the corner. It was a trophy-room of some sort. She pushed open the door and went inside. Silver cups, bronze statuettes, rose bowls, shields and medallions filled every conceivable space. When she peered closer to read the inscriptions she realised that they were the spoils from Marc's career—rewards for his many years as an international racing driver.

She lingered, wondering just how he felt now, having given it all up. His life must have changed dramatically that June day three years ago. Though not a follower of that particular sport herself, even Sarella had a vague recollection of what had happened once Peter had jogged her memory.

It had been an horrific triple crash that had left two drivers dead, and the newsreel of that dreadful moment had shown a blazing object being catapulted clear of the wreckage. That object had been Marc Vila. Nobody had expected him to live.

Peter told her how he had hovered on the margin of death for nearly six months. When he had at last regained consciousness no one had expected him to be more than a vegetable. But he had learned to walk, to think, to live like anybody else. He did it through sheer will-power, Peter had told her admiringly. That was before she met him.

Now, remembering all this, she wondered how she'd had the temerity to stand up to him that morning. He was more formidable and, leaving aside the way he had treated her, more admirable in so many other ways than any man she had ever encountered. No wonder poor Peter was so much in awe of him!

Still, she thought as she closed the door of the trophy-room, it doesn't give him the right to treat me like—— She bit off the dreadful word that sprang to mind. Whatever he said, it wasn't fair. She wasn't like that. And she wasn't going to rest until he'd revised his opinion of her.

She made her way downstairs with the idea of going into the sitting-room to watch the news. There was a satellite dish out in the grounds, and she was keen to keep up her French and Spanish as they had improved no end since she had begun working in Peter's cosmopolitan little shop at the resort.

But she had just settled down, flicking the control through a dozen or so channels until she found the one she wanted, when the door opened and Marc himself came in. He carried a phone, and when he saw her he held it out to her. 'Call for you.'

As soon as she took it he went over to the window and stood gazing out at the rain.

It was Peter. 'Love,' he said, 'how are things? Have you told big brother what you think of him yet?'

'No——' she wanted to tell him it wouldn't be diplomatic, but it was no good going into the events of the day with Marc hovering within earshot '—things are all right. I miss you,' she added for Marc's benefit. 'When are you coming back? Are you on your way?'

'Hasn't he told you?'

Her heart plummeted. 'Who? What?'

'I just told Marc a minute ago. I can't get back right now.'

'But you promised, Peter! You said you'd come back straight away——'

'Listen—it's not as easy as that. You know why. What am I going to say to him when I turn up empty-handed?'

'I thought you'd already worked that out?'

'I thought I had. But it's not so easy to persuade people to do what you want—not when they're pillars of society!'

'What on earth do you mean?'

'I thought the notary might have backdated an agreement, but of course he won't.'

'Of course he won't!' She was amazed the thought had even entered his head.

'So what now?' he asked.

'I don't know! I didn't get us into this mess——' She broke off with a guilty look over her shoulder. Marc was gazing out of the window, but he couldn't help overhearing her side of the conversation. She could have taken the phone up to her room, but she felt too annoyed with Peter to want to prolong the call. 'When do you imagine you'll get back?' she asked, tight-lipped.

'As soon as ever I can, love.'

'I see.'

'Don't worry, I'll think of something.'

'Where are you now?' she asked as she thought she heard voices in the background.

There was a slight hesitation, then he admitted, 'I'm in France. There wasn't much point in calling in at the shop, so I came straight here.'

'To friends?'

'You sound like a jealous wife,' he remarked flippantly.

'I'm not. I'm just curious.'

'I'll tell you everything when I get back. There is

something I should have told you. Will you forgive me, love?'

Sarella frowned. Her misgivings sprang to life again. 'It depends what it is.'

'It'll make you understand how much your help means to me. But I can't go into details now. Trust me—that's all I ask.'

'I do—at least, I'm trying to. But I'm beginning to wonder whether it's a good idea.'

What he had just done was sentence her to another day of hell. She said in a quiet whisper so that Marc wouldn't overhear, 'I can't stand much more of your brother, Peter. I'm warning you. Come back soon, otherwise I can't guarantee I shall be here much longer.'

'Please, sweetheart, hang on in there. It won't be long now. You can do it. Please, for my sake,' he wheedled.

She hated it when men started to act cute, pleading like little lost boys. She said shortly, 'I'll give you another twenty-four hours.'

'Then what? You'll leave? But where will you go?'

'The apartment, of course—where else?'

She heard the relief in his voice. 'That's OK, then.'

She rang off almost straight away. Great. So she could find her own way back to the apartment and hole up there, could she, while he did heaven knew what in France?

'Problems?' asked a deep voice from by the window. She gave a start. So absorbed by what Peter had told her, she had almost forgotten that Marc was still in the room.

He was smiling grimly now as he came towards her. 'The course of true love never did run smooth. Delectable though you are, even you can't change the fact that Peter has never understood exactly what the word "fidelity" means.'

'What on earth do you mean?' She stepped back, the phone buzzing against the side of her face.

'What's he doing in France, I wonder? Never mind, you'll probably be able to try for breach of promise. I'm sure you're already working it out.'

'*What?*'

'Aren't you?' He raised two cynical brows.

'I don't know what you mean. I don't understand this world.' She was suddenly in alien territory again, being accused of being somebody she could never be, except on stage with a script in her hand.

'Peter means well and people always forgive him for his little failures. But I would have thought you'd expect him to be faithful to you for a day or two at least.'

'He's a free agent——' she blurted. 'I mean——'

'A free agent? How very sophisticated of you! This is going to be a very modern marriage, Sarella.'

'You don't understand,' she blurted, thoroughly confused.

'Look, give up now,' Marc persisted. 'Let me check the flights back to London for you. Get yourself out of it. There's obviously nothing in it for you on any level at all.'

Sarella ran a hand over her face, toying with the phone, then moving away out of range so that she had time to think. If he only knew how desperate she was to get away now that Peter had crystallised all her doubts. But when she turned she was smiling. 'I would expect you to try to poison my mind against him. No doubt you tried the same thing with him—implying that we'd got along rather better than we ought to have?' That would account for Peter's evasiveness. It was suddenly as clear as day.

Marc gave a laugh. 'I'm going up to change for dinner. See you at eight.' With no more than a rather cryptic smile he went out, leaving her to the turmoil of thoughts that were no longer as crystal-clear as she had tried to make him believe.

Tomorrow, she decided, if Peter doesn't get back I'll have to leave. I really will. Marc was simply too dangerous to be near. Although she hated him, she knew something else was beginning to flower. It was something to do with what she had discovered in her exploration of the trophy-room—a grudging respect, an admiration for his courage and integrity, for his sheer will to survive. But there was also, despite the overt antagonism between them, a growing closeness too. She would have to be blind not to be aware of it. It was as if these verbal skirmishes had a deeper meaning. They were almost a pleasure, like a courting dance, only time delaying the inevitable climax.

If Peter doesn't come back tomorrow I'll go to the apartment in Soldeu, she told herself. If he wants to explain things to me he'll have to come there to find me.

With this firmly decided, she made her way up to change out of the trousers and sweater she had been wearing all that long day.

CHAPTER FIVE

WHEN Sarella pushed open the big old doors of the refectory a few minutes after eight she found the high-domed room beyond her deserted. But, as she stood undecidedly on the threshold, Marc appeared through a door at the far end. 'We're dining in the conservatory this evening,' he told her, strolling the length of the room towards her. 'It's cosier than here. Follow me.' But instead of turning to go he watched as she moved towards him.

Conscious of his enigmatic scrutiny, she wondered if he always ordered his guests about in a series of curt commands. His harsh manner was at odds with his appearance—sleek black hair lay in gentle waves, and even when he wasn't running his hands through it it always looked windblown like now, making him seem casual and relaxed. He only looks laid back, she criticised to herself; it's a front. He's an uptight devil, only interested in giving orders and having them obeyed. Now, she judged, his informal look was due only to the casual style of his clothes, a linen jacket in a beige loose-weave designed to set off his sexy tan, and a sort of hand-spun silk T-shirt emphasising the solid muscle underneath. It gave him that *Vogue*-ish look that belonged to his life as an international racing star.

'Very chic,' he observed in his gravelly voice after this mutual appraisal. It was as if he was echoing her own grudging appraisal. His glance had never left her as she'd tapped towards him across the mirror-like floor, dark eyes sweeping her from head to toe to take in her black high-heeled shoes, black stockings and the stark simplicity of the black wool dress skimming her knees, with a sardonic half-smile.

She had tried to soften the effect of long sleeves and a high round neck with a pair of pearl stud earrings. Not having brought any jewellery with her when she'd first come to Andorra on that long-ago skiing holiday, she hadn't bothered to buy any. She didn't lead the sort of life where jewellery was a requisite. But Peter had insisted on giving her the earrings as an engagement present, with the promise that a ring would soon follow. Sarella had protested, not feeling happy about taking anything from him, but he had insisted. This was the first chance she'd had to wear them; last night things had been too fraught to think of dressing up, and now they were her only adornment.

'Very chic indeed,' Marc murmured again in that husky bass. She felt her toes curl, but couldn't help giving him a sharp glance. Was he being patronising, needling or what? His expression was that familiar give-nothing-away blank now that the smile had mysteriously vanished.

'Thank you,' she said levelly as she walked past him through the door he held open.

Then she faltered on the threshold. Cosy, had he said? Even if cosy wasn't the word she would have applied to the conservatory opening out before her she could see it was a little more intimate than the vast medieval refectory in which they'd previously dined.

A table for two had been set in a sort of bower beneath a canopy of spreading palms. But beyond that intimate corner was a wall of translucent glass, giving an uninterrupted view of the mountains. Lights were already beginning to diamond out of the shadowed pine woods on the lower slopes.

She stifled a gasp of pure pleasure.

Marc seemed unaware of the effect of this spectacular setting. But, as he pulled out her chair and let his fingers skim as if by accident across her shoulders, red lights started to flash a warning. He knew very well what he was doing. She'd be a fool to forget it.

Tonight he certainly seemed at pains to play the perfect host. The table looked exquisite, and there was even a rose—a yellow one—lying across her plate. Yellow for jealousy? she struggled to recall. He would be unlikely to know the old-fashioned symbolism of flowers. He wasn't the type.

When he took his place opposite, the small table seemed suddenly more intimate still—dangerously so. She began to tremble.

Luckily a team of waiters offered a line of protection, though even they could do nothing about the way he was levelling those dark eyes at her as if with deliberate and enigmatic meaning.

When they were eventually left alone, with the food spread on old china so thin that it was almost transparent, he leaned forward with a show of curiosity and murmured, 'Are they real? Forgive the question. . . I shouldn't ask. But they complement the bloom of your skin to perfection.' His fingers came out and hovered at the side of her head.

Disconcerted, Sarella put up a hand to her earrings. 'These? I don't know whether they're real. I shouldn't think so!' She laughed, confused by his intent expression. Then a blush flew up her neck. Heavens! She hadn't even thought! 'I wouldn't know how to tell,' she managed to say.

'I would. I've become something of a connoisseur now that I'm more housebound than of old. I'll look at them later if you like.' His expression didn't change.

'Thank you,' she mumbled into her plate. Her mind was in confusion. What if they were real? she wondered. They would be worth thousands! Oh, no, she prayed silently, surely Peter hadn't blithely handed over one of the family heirlooms? Marc would lap up the opportunity to use it against her. And what could she say in self-defence?

'Tell me about your acting career,' he invited with an abrupt change of topic as if to say the matter of the earrings was forgotten, though she knew it wasn't. 'You're taking rather a long rest, aren't you?'

She nodded. 'I needed time to decide what to do about my career,' she admitted. Why not be frank? He wouldn't believe her anyway.

'What have you appeared in, then? Anything I might have seen?'

'That depends on whether you spend much time in London,' she hedged.

He shook his head, avoiding her glance. 'Not enough at the moment, unluckily. But things will change.'

There was a pause as if he had said more than he had intended, and, not wanting to probe, she went on, 'After drama school I landed a role in a long-running West End farce, as the dumb blonde—because of my looks, I suppose. It was quite fun, actually. I became quite a celebrity because of it. I stayed with it for three months, then left because it wasn't what I wanted to spend my life doing. Luckily I managed to get a job with a small fit-up touring company—playing small theatres in the provinces, living in digs, away from the spotlight and very badly paid. But it was enormously exciting. We played a different town every week. I learned an awful lot about audiences and what they want.' Marc was very still, just watching her, and, unable to tell what he was thinking, she went on, 'It was hard work but worth-while—a real challenge.' As she spoke her eyes came alive, but now she broke off.

Before she could continue he said, 'So what made you leave?' Despite the question, there was still that same blank expression on his face.

Sarella forced herself to ignore it and replied, 'The company lost its grant and we had to split up. I had no choice but to leave.'

'So you found yourself out of work. I see.'

He seemed to 'see' far more than her words suggetsed. 'I'd been working solidly for eighteen months,' she pointed out. 'I simply had to have a break. In some ways it was a welcome turn of events. I thought it was a good time to get away and take stock.'

'And?'

'And what?'

'How does it follow from what you've said that you came to be——' He paused and his lips compressed in a cruelly thin line before he seemed to deliberately force away the tension, saying simply, 'To be with my brother?'

She held his glance. 'I saw the advert for a job in Peter's shop. That break had made me realise I wasn't in control of my career. I didn't know whether to go back and try for something in the West End again, or television, films—or even go back into fringe theatre. Offers were coming in, but I didn't know what I wanted. I needed time to sort out my values.' She bit her lip. Here she was, not even halfway through the soup, and she was telling Marc things she hadn't even told Peter. Her career was important to her, and he had no idea.

'Are you still in a state of indecision?' he probed when she didn't go on.

She shook her head. 'No. But then, it's not as simple

as that. I might have made a mistake to turn down offers when they were there. I'm not sure they still are. The choice might no longer be in my hands.'

'You have an agent?'

She nodded.

'So it's a case of out of sight, out of mind?'

She nodded again. 'Maybe. I don't know.'

'Obviously you should get back as soon as possible.'

Sarella hated him for putting it so starkly. 'I always intended to go back after my two months at the shop were up.'

'But Peter intervened?'

She nodded. How could she tell him that Peter's 'intervention' had only been supposed to take up a week of her time? She'd told him she'd have to go back to work and he had laughingly agreed, making some quip about being escort to a star and hitting the gossip columns. He hadn't really understood that it was work to her.

'You can ring your agent tomorrow morning,' said Marc, taking her by surprise. 'You never know, he may have something for you.'

Sarella raised her eyes to his. Was he being charitable for once, or was it another attempt to get her out of Peter's life? 'Peter should be back tomorrow.' She meant that, once she had talked him into releasing her from this crazy engagement, she would be free to take up her own life once more. But Marc misunderstood.

His face was expressionless when he said, 'I expect you're feeling pretty miserable about things just now. It always surprises me how eagerly women fall for his boyish charm. I would have thought it was obvious to anyone that he never thinks further than the pleasures of the next few minutes. He's still a child. Emotionally immature.'

'You're convinced he's already with someone else, aren't you?' She was half convinced herself. Popping over the border into France had been Peter's favourite excuse to account for his absences from the shop ever since she'd known him. But why hadn't he told her the truth? A hundred other questions begged to be answered.

'It's no good fooling yourself, is it?' Marc's black eyes never left her face. Though his words were brutal, his tone seemed to have softened. She thought it unlikely that this was due to concern for her feelings—it would be a new departure for him to accept that she might have any, apart from avarice.

But then he said, 'Despite your own ability to say no to the pleasures of the moment, I suppose you must be feeling rather hurt.' He spread a hand to include their intimate little world. 'Perhaps this will take your mind off things for a while? If there's anything else I can do,' he went on, 'you only have to ask.'

She shook her head at once and, keeping her voice level, replied, 'There's nothing you can do for me, but thanks for the offer. . .'

In return he gave a short laugh. 'I didn't mean what you obviously think I meant. It was a genuine expression of sympathy. I'm not totally without feelings——' Then he broke off with a frown and added, 'Though, as the most obnoxious specimen you've ever met in your entire life, I can't expect you to believe that.'

His dark eyes glinted in the candlelight, but was it with amusement or anger? He was an enigma, his feelings hidden deep behind a sophisticated defence-work of cynicism and distrust.

What had made him like this? she pondered. Surely it wasn't a simple distrust of herself? It seemed somehow deeper, as if its roots lay hidden in the past.

He interrupted her thoughts and showed he was himself still on the same track, for he observed, 'I've been called many things in my time, but never a bully, or,' he frowned again, 'a megalomaniac out of a horror movie.'

Sarella failed to stifle a sudden smile. 'I *am* sorry— that was rather over the top, wasn't it? I was feeling so angry with you. . .' She broke off. The fact that Marc had registered her exact words seemed to say that they meant something—that he hadn't simply dismissed what she had yelled out from the shower, but that he had remembered and, as it seemed now, had brooded over them for some time. She recalled all the other outrageous things she had called him. 'At that moment I meant every word,' she admitted candidly. 'You really did seem horrible. And I was furious with you!'

'And now?' The question was so silkily inserted that she drew in a breath.

'*Now?*' She gulped. 'I suppose——' she shot him a quick glance '—I suppose, to be honest, nothing has really changed under the surface, has it?'

He pretended to do a double-take. 'You mean, despite the rose, the candlelight and the unsurpassable view, not to mention this rather excellent wine from my own cellars, you still regard me as Bluebeard?'

He caught her eye and their glances locked, and for a moment everything outside their golden circle seemed to fade. He was so handsome, so present—it was a warmth and vitality that only his immense rage had masked, making her lash out in self-defence, but now that it was turned to a kind of gentle humour, and—she had to admit it—a single-minded interest in her she found him dangerously attractive. She felt safe only when he was treating her with his customary icy rage. And memory, too, came crowding back, recalling the harsh things he had said with no sign of regret or subsequent apology. He must have seen the laughter die in her eyes, for he said tonelessly, 'I see.'

'You don't see,' she contradicted at once, her manner suddenly earnest. 'You don't see at all. But one day you will. You'll know all those things you said were untrue. And then——' She felt her glance slide away to the distant peaks across the valley. And then what? It would be too late for them. They would have lost each other. Nothing was ever going to come of it. How could she harbour the slightest hope?

'And then?' he prompted, his eyes fixed intently on her face.

'And then you'll see,' she said weakly.

There was a pause. The candle guttered in its crystal holder, sending shadows dancing mysteriously over the hollows of his face. 'I wonder what I'll see?' His lips twisted in a smile that was halfway between pain and sorrow.

When he spoke again, after one of the maids had cleared away the remains of the main course and brought in a magnificent charlotte russe, his manner had changed. He was now at his most ironic. 'It says something for the civilising effect of our upbringing that we can both sit here calmly sharing a meal together when we freely admit to the same deep-seated and violent antipathy.'

There was no answer to that. Sarella swallowed the delicious concoction placed before her without tasting it. It required an effort to conceal the sharp stab of pain his words had caused, but she agreed with a light, 'Three cheers for upbringing. Where was yours done?'

'Biography time,' he observed with a dry smile as if he'd done this dinner-table routine with countless women before. 'Hong Kong until I was six, then board-ing-school in England,' he replied without any attempt to conceal how bored he felt. 'And you?' His eyes kindled. 'Let's talk about you.'

'Just England,' she admitted, not wishing to go into details and wondering why he was so reticent about his own life.

'The succinct Miss—— Hey!' His eyes flashed again. 'I don't even know your second name.'

'Jones,' she replied shortly.

'Stage name or real name?'

'My imagination isn't so impoverished that I would invent a name like Jones,' she came back. If she kept everything on this level there would be no danger of his probing into her background. She had nothing to hide, except the dull ordinariness of her life before drama school, but for him to know about it would only bring them closer, and she recoiled from the danger that that would lead to. Besides, he would only make it grist to his mill. She knew she was still on trial, despite his efforts to appear at ease.

He was laughing, handsome and dazzling again. 'Sarella Jones. I doubt whether you could improve on that. It sounds good. Better than Sarella Vila!'

'I already know that's what you think,' she observed with an ironic shrug.

'Oh, Peter, you mean,' he said as if he'd forgotten all about him. 'Of course.' He gave her a strange look, and she wondered why he had called her Sarella Vila if he'd already forgotten about Peter. And then she wondered if he was thinking the same about her—how on earth could any woman forget she was about to change her name? Unless, of course, she had no intention of doing any such thing. . .

To forestall further awkward questions she asked, 'Do you racing drivers really enjoy all the danger?'

Marc stopped laughing and for a moment his eyes darkened. 'Sure. Until it catches up with you. Then you start to think there's something crazy about living life only to lose it. And then,' he sighed, 'you start to acquire other more staid and sensible interests.' He flashed her a crooked smile. 'I enjoy driving fast cars, but I don't miss the superficial adulation that goes with it.'

His eyes were so alive that she felt she was looking straight into the source of his pleasure—he was the sort of man who thrived on challenge and went out to meet it head-on. It made something sting behind her eyes as she thought now that it was all finished for him.

He read at once what was in her mind and his manner softened. 'Hey, don't look like that.' He reached abruptly across the table and placed one hand over hers. 'No one can go on forever. I came to terms with that long before the accident. All it meant was that my career came to an end slightly ahead of schedule.' A shadow swooped across his face and vanished. 'Are you acting, Sarella, when you give me that look of—whatever it is?' His brows drew together in a frown. 'I don't think I can tell when you're acting. You look so vulnerable, as if you care deeply about—— Hey, you are *good*!' His mouth hardened and he gave a laugh. 'You're *very* good,' he said abruptly. 'I suppose it's difficult for you to stop acting. Just as I can never stop competing. It's ingrained in us. . .' He surveyed her through narrowed eyes. 'I suppose you must know you look like a painting, a madonna—— Damn it, you're pulling my reason all ways, Sarella. What the hell am I supposed to make of you? I should throw you out now and have done with it. Instead. . .'

Her hand throbbed beneath his where he still trapped

it on the table. She longed to turn it, to open her palm to the completeness of his touch, but her feelings warred within her again. If he admitted to being confused then so was she. His look seemed to give evidence of something stirring in his emotions, and it was as unexpected as it was difficult to believe. But he was still under the impression that she was after Peter for his inheritance. He hadn't backed down on that. Her throat constricted and she swallowed hard before stammering, 'I—I don't know what you mean. I'm not acting.'

He kept her hand imprisoned beneath his for an endless moment before carefully removing it and picking up his wine glass. Gazing into it, he seemed to consider his words carefully. Then he said, 'It would be quite an achievement to have both Peter and myself paying court to you. Who would finish up as victor ludorum?'

'I think it's most unlikely that either you or Peter would ever pay court to any woman for longer than it suited you. In that respect you're both master gamesplayers.' Sarella spoke all on one tone, trying to pretend she hadn't been knocked sideways by the sudden intensity of Marc's mood. It was only another instance of his drive to gain control, she told herself. Her nerves were worn ragged by the swift changes in his moods, as first they convinced her of his avowed antipathy, as he called it, and then somehow, without any warning, he seemed to be saying quite the opposite. She didn't know where she was.

Now he was getting up and coming round the table towards her. 'Let's have our brandies on the terrace. It's probably warm enough.'

Relieved to find some respite from the intensity of the last few moments, she allowed him to guide her outside.

The sky was navy blue, pricked by planets and a scatter of stars. She shivered a little, leaning on the balustrade and looking down into the darkness while he gave some instructions to the maid. When he came back he put a wrap round her shoulders. 'How is it?' he murmured. 'Too cold?'

'It's all right.' Perhaps the cold would cool things between them? He kept one arm round her shoulders, and she couldn't help leaning in towards him. They stood like that for a moment, neither of them moving.

They were wrapped in night. When Marc spoke his words seemed to grow out of the night itself. His voice was husky when he said, 'I don't think I can keep my hands off you much longer, Sarella. . .What are you going to do, darling?'

All thought skipped from her mind. The pause lengthened.

'Sarella, answer me.' The fingers on her shoulder didn't move, but his voice thickened as if his emotions were suddenly too strong to be concealed.

It was worse than before, when he had taken her so powerfully into his arms and she had felt him thieve unresisting kisses from her lips, for now he was playing with her heart, not just her senses, and it was, she found, a vulnerable organ, halfway to belonging to him already.

'Answer me. What are you going to do?' he repeated. He turned his gleaming black head to her, his face close enough to touch, the wide mouth inviting surrender to its irresistible demands.

A chorus of voices ordered her to give in. Only a lone voice, that of common sense, warned her to draw back while there was still time.

She could feel the hard muscles of his body pressing against her side, his arm sheltering her in a way that made her trust him. Would it be so wrong to give in? argued the voices in her head. Why not say yes? Love him? You know you want to. Where's the harm?

Common sense tried to argue against them. Remember what he called you only this morning? it said. Was he right after all? Are you going to prove it? Go ahead, admonished the voice, but see if you can look yourself in the eye tomorrow morning.

With she knew not what power of self-denial Sarella tried to edge away so that Marc's body wasn't pressing so vibrantly against her own. It was a movement small but eloquent. Even so, she could feel the heat of his desire drawing her back to him, sapping her will to resist. She began to tremble again, the strain too much. How could she tell him she was unable to trust him? As it was, he made the decisive next move. With a regretful sigh he removed his arm from its protective place around her shoulders and stepped back. Avoiding her glance, he leaned against the parapet round the terrace, facing towards the lights of the house so that his expression was picked out in fine detail. She could see the small scar on his right cheek and the firm jaw and the paleness of his face as he struggled with some inner demon. There was a nerve at the side of his mouth quivering with the effort of control.

She felt that the slightest movement would snap his will, precipitating an explosion out of the swell of desire that was sweeping them both to the edge of a world they were too prudent to enter willingly.

Oh, God, help me resist, she cried inwardly. Let him not take me in his arms. Please save me from wrong. . . Even as she prayed for deliverance, her body shook with the desire to be one with him. What she could not see was what was in his mind. He was as much in control of his private thoughts as ever. All she had was the conviction that he desired her, despite himself.

But he gave a sudden jerk of his head. 'Why, Sarella?'

he grated after a battle that seemed to draw itself out to the limits. 'Why is this happening to us?'

He swivelled and in one swift movement gripped her jaw between his fingers and lifted her mouth to his, raking his pirating lips over it again and again, a groan of deep desire wrenched from the depths of his being. The world seemed to shiver into a million splinters of prismatic colour, silent and fiery, so that they themselves seemed to become beings other than themselves, inhabitants of another planet, out of time.

She felt her knees begin to buckle, but his strength held her to him—taking her fevered body into his embrace, heaping fire on fire until she was crying for him in a voice unlike her own.

Then as quickly as the conflagration had taken hold it was doused. She could feel the moment when he decided to thrust her away from him, abruptly stepping back, the shock of their coming apart striking as swift as a blow, stunning her, so that she fell back against the parapet, her lips swollen by the passion of his taking, a soft anguished breath escaping from between them.

'Why?' he rasped again as his eyes scoured her face for an answer. His lips were drawn back and his eyes flashed as one fist smashed hard on to the top of the snow-covered wall.

Blankly staring at the print, a visible record of his inner conflict, Sarella reeled forward, arms outstretched.

But he brushed her aside. 'This is what you want, isn't it? Now that Peter is safely out of the way. . .now that you've reassessed the potential of Rocamar!' He threw back his head and gave a harsh bellow.

'Marc, no——!' She stopped, unable to believe the sound that croaked from between her own lips. He was breaking her on his wheel of fire, forcing her with him to a high-point of surrender, then casting her away as if her touch were a contamination.

'Don't recount your excuses to me. We're both people of the world, equals on the road to folly. I'm a man and you're a beautiful woman—beautiful and inevitably scheming.' He gave another hollow laugh and swivelled towards the main door. 'Let's just——' He paused, his voice blurring to a savage growl. He began again, 'What are you intending to do for the rest of the evening?' he rasped. 'Watch a movie?' He gestured inside. 'I've got things to look over in my office.' With a jerking movement he turned to the house and pushed his way inside.

Her glance flew after him, watching as he shouldered past the clutching fingers of the palms until he disappeared through the far door.

So that was that. His abrupt departure left her close to collapse. It tore her heart to see him go.

A few minutes later she heard the rich throb of a car engine in the drive below. Leaning forward, she was in time to see a lethal-looking sports car nose its way across the cobbles. In a moment it was sliding over the drawbridge and a few seconds later she saw its red tail-lights disappearing at speed down the mountainside towards the outside world. So much for the things Marc had to look over, she thought wretchedly. But then, what did she expect? He still imagined she was acting, even when she had never been more painfully herself.

But surely, she asked herself, he could tell the difference? She screamed in an uproar of inward misery. Couldn't anyone tell she was crazy for him and further from acting a role than at any time in her entire life?

Somehow she made her way down to the library, picked out the Dietrich films and forced herself to watch them until the early hours. Even though she tried to

listen out for the sound of a returning car, the castle and
the road leading up to it remained as silent as the grave.

Peter was on the line. Sarella held the phone against her
cheek with the rest of her face buried in the pillow and
tried to guess what time it was.

'You sound a bit dim this morning,' he said in
greeting.

'I was asleep,' she explained blearily.

'With big brother?'

'Certainly not!'

'He's losing his touch. Or does he still pretend he
objects to being called Bluebeard?'

'Ask him yourself,' she suggested, trying to clear her
head.

'Put him on, then.'

'How?' she glanced at the complicated internal phone
system beside the bed.

'You mean he really *isn't* there?'

'Of course he's damn well not!' Now that Sarella was
waking up she was beginning to feel furious. There was
a great black cloud hovering over her head. It made
everything seem hopeless. 'I'm leaving this place, Peter.
I've had enough. I need to be back in London to get
work,' she told him. At least last night had clarified
something. 'You seem to forget I have a career to think
about.' Fragments of last night's conversation taunted
her.

But Peter said, 'You'll be lucky.'

Now what? Her heart sank. What annoying snag had
cropped up this time? 'What do you mean?'

'Have you looked out of the window?'

'I haven't had a chance. Why?' She raised her head.
There was a bluish glow from outside.

'Complete white-out,' he told her cheerily. 'So I've decided to stay on a bit. The roads are impassable.'

'You mean you're going skiing!'

'Have a heart! It's got to be the last fall of the season!'

'Peter? Do you really mean this? You mean you're leaving me here with that man while you enjoy yourself on the ski-slopes? I don't believe I'm hearing this! You *can't*!' The full horror of last night had come rushing back, giving shape and dimension to the sense of despair she had carried with her out of sleep.

But Peter was unaware of all this. 'Keep calm,' he advised. 'If you've any sense you'll grab a pair of skis and do the same. It's brilliant powder. Couldn't be better.'

'Peter——'

'Sorry, love. Have to go before it gets ruined by the day-trippers.'

'But, Peter——'

But he had already rung off. Sarella lay fuming in bed for a few minutes before flinging back the duvet and running to the window. He was right—a thick blanket of snow had turned the scene outside into a picture-postcard. 'Damn you, Peter; damn you!' she breathed.

Now what? She had to get away, now more than ever. But even her earlier resolve to leave Castell Rocamar at the earliest was on the line—especially now that there was a chance Peter wouldn't even try to make it back today.

Were the roads really as impassable as he claimed? She couldn't tell from her vantage-point up here in the tower. Ominously, she couldn't even see the road when she peered down out of the high window. It looked as if she was well and truly trapped.

Hurriedly showering and pulling on the same pair of jeans she had worn the day she'd arrived, she jerked a baggy sweater over her head and went downstairs. There was nobody around, and she had to unlock the enormous oak doors herself, using both hands to turn the iron key, then pushing one of the doors open, her shoulder against it, before she was able to see outside.

Snow was banked behind it, dredging against the bottom as she pushed it open. As she managed to peer round it her heart sank. The scene was transformed into a wilderness of dazzling white. Drifts three or four feet high lay within the castle walls. Nothing could get out—or in, she registered with a flicker of hope. But it was pointless to look for tell-tale tyre marks in this.

Dragging the door shut, she made her way towards the stairs. Maybe she should pack. Now might be her best chance to escape while Peter was still away. The servants would know whether it was possible to get back down the valley. Surely later in the morning it might be OK? She might even pass him on the way up! Once back in town she would be able to find some form of public transport. She would do it! She would get away from here as soon as the snow began to melt.

With this intention firmly planted in her mind, she headed for the back stairs leading down into the kitchens. Her feet tapped loudly on the curving stone steps and for a moment she felt like a bit-player descending to the dungeons—with horror, and a stack of movie cameras, lying ahead. The reality was quite different. There was only the French chef Pierre, whistling between his teeth as he pounded something aromatic in a pestle, and a couple of aproned maids bustling about with what looked like preparations for breakfast.

After a brief greeting Sarella asked in halting French about the state of the roads. Pierre spread his arms and raised his glance to the ceiling. 'Impossible!' And when he saw her look of consternation he added, 'But no worry—we 'ave plenty 'ere.' He swept his arms round to include every cranny of the well-stocked kitchen.

'How long do you think it will last?' she enunciated.

He shrugged helplessly. ''Oo knows? One, two, ten days maybe.'

She beat a retreat when she realised that she was going to get nothing further out of him. It had been uppermost in her mind to ask about Marc, but her courage failed her at the last. He couldn't have got back last night. The snow had obviously been falling for hours, probably while she was still watching *The Blue Angel*.

Breakfast, when not taken in the kitchen, was in an ante-room off the refectory. Everything was arranged on an oak buffet against the wall. It was while she was standing at it, buttering some toast, that Sarella heard someone humming outside. Despite the snow, the window was open, the central-heating system coping easily with the vagaries of the climate. It was the theme from last night's film that floated up to her.

She matched the words to the melody. As a silent duet it was just as haunting. And the words happened to be so very true. . .

She moved to the window. At this place the terrace was inaccessible, being several feet below the level of the room, and her first glimpse was of the back of a dark head down below. Even before he turned she knew who it was. So he had come back. Sarella felt a jolt through her entire body at the sight of him.

With some telepathy at work, his questing glance came to rest in the exact square of window in which her face appeared. Their eyes met. The melancholy song died away. For a moment she was too surprised to speak and simply stared as if she were looking down on an apparition.

Then he waded through the banked snow to the foot of the wall. 'Sleep well?' he called up.

With the piece of toast in her hand she went right up to the window and pushed it further open. Calling on her skills, she matched his coolness, saying simply, 'Yes, thanks.'

But he said surprisingly, 'I was going to wake you, but relented in time.'

'Wake me?'

He treated her to his special smile. 'Curled up asleep in front of Dietrich.'

'Was I?'

'Your eyes were shut.'

'I must have been resting them,' she protested.

'And you didn't hear me come in.'

Her glance skimmed his face to detect the truth. 'I——Did you?'

'Nor what happened then.'

Sarella leaned out. 'What did happen?' His expression was grim and her heart was bumping wildly.

His eyes, now that she could see them clearly, abraded her flesh with a cold more searing than the icy wind blowing up from the valley this morning. It was such a shock to feel his animosity directed so unwaveringly towards her; even though, after last night, she could have been prepared for something, she could only gape down at him. His few words scarcely made any sense to her. But there was something unmistakably hostile in their tone.

'Finish your breakfast.' He dismissed her by turning and wading back round the corner of the wall.

She was pushing a piece of toast around on her plate, wondering if she had imagined that arctic expression on his face just now, when she heard the door open. Knowing who it was without raising her head, she waited until she felt him standing beside her, but when she looked up, already prepared for trouble, she was shocked by the intensity of the hatred that glittered from out of his eyes.

Without saying anything, he held out a fist and then, as she watched, mesmerised, he slowly opened his fingers to reveal something lying in the palm. It was a pair of pearl earrings. Her earrings.

'Well?' she managed to question, forcing her chin up.

'They were on the arm of the chair you were sitting in last night. When you were "resting" your eyes.' He didn't smile. In fact, his voice was metallic, cutting as honed steel, sending a paralysing chill through her bones.

'So——?' she managed to breathe.

'Thirty thousand pounds' worth of Regency pearls. And you didn't even notice I'd taken them!'

'I——' She swallowed. There was nothing she could say to excuse herself—except the truth. 'I'd no idea they were so valuable,' she gulped. Her head swam.

He raised his black eyebrows in a look so disbelieving that she could only repeat what she'd said. But the more she defended herself, the more unreliable she sounded.

Marc pocketed the earrings and leaned forward with one hand on the table in front of her. 'I'm keeping them. If you want to make a fight of it I should warn you that they were not his to give. They're family property.'

'I didn't know,' Sarella said dully in a last-ditch attempt to salvage something from the wreckage of her self-esteem.

'That's something yet to be proven.' He removed his hand and she lifted her head, thinking he was about to leave. But he gave her a smouldering glance and said, 'This change in the weather couldn't have come at a worse time. I want you out of here just as much as you

must want to go. The most painful——' He paused,
corrected a slip of the tongue, and went on, 'The most
painless way is for us to keep out of each other's way
until you can leave. I'm taking my meals elsewhere. As
soon as it's possible I'll have a car take you to the airport.
Whether you want to or not, you're leaving here just as
soon as it can be arranged. And, Sarella, I suggest you
go without making any waves—I can get up quite a case
against you. I can buy the best legal brains in the
business, so it's no use your fighting. Get it?'

Unable to bear the injustice of it any further, she
scraped back her chair and rose to her feet. 'You think I
talked Peter into giving me those earrings, don't you?
You think I tried to steal your family heirlooms, don't
you? You do, don't you? *Answer me!*' she shouted when
he didn't say anything. 'Say it to me! Don't just stand
there with that hateful expression on your face!'

And when he still didn't say anything she went up to
him and shouted into his face, 'You think I'm a slut and
a common thief! You can't see past your own stupid
blind prejudice! You think you know everything about
everyone! Well, you don't! You don't know a blind
thing! You're so twisted with suspicion that you can't
see a hand in front of your face without imagining there's
a dagger in it! Why should I want your filthy rotten
possessions? I don't care a damn about this place, or
you, or what you own. You're nothing, do you hear me?
When I called you a pompous, self-opinionated bully I
meant every word! You're not only obnoxious, you're
sick! You admit you hate me, yet it didn't stop you from
practically raping me when you thought you could get
away with it. I call that really sick! And I'll tell you one
more thing, Mr Oh, so famous Vila, if you want to get
rid of me, you can't begin to imagine how much I want

to be rid of you! I want you and everything to do with you out of my life for good!'

Tears of rage were gushing from her eyes by now. With one last blinding cry of pain she brushed past him and ran from the room.

CHAPTER SIX

MARC was as good as his word and Sarella saw no more of him that day. By early evening she was desperate. Her outburst had at least got some of her anger off her chest, but she was still a prisoner, and when fresh falls of snow were forecast she felt near the end of her tether at the prospect of being trapped any longer at Rocamar. It didn't help to admit that, but for her own stupidity, she would never have come near the place.

All attempts to contact Peter failed. After a restless night, she tried again next morning, but with no more success. As she replaced the receiver after the last attempt she remembered Marc's suggestion two days ago. She dialled London.

'Beryl? Thank goodness!'

Her agent, bless her, recognised her voice instantly. 'Darling, when the hell are you coming back? I've got a million people screaming down the line for you. Two months, you said. Your time's up. What am I supposed to tell them?' Then Beryl went on to outline a couple of job offers that had come in within the last few days.

She was a big, bosomy woman who couldn't work without a box of biscuits on the desk beside her, and Sarella could hear her now, crunching her way through them. There had always been a sympathetic ear for her clients, and she longed to pour out all her troubles right away. But Beryl was busy.

'Tell you what I'll do, lovey,' she was saying. 'I'm going to get right back to these producers and let 'em know you're back in the picture. Give me your number and I'll dial as soon as I've had a word. Got another couple of clients in the office right now, but we'll have a good heart-to-heart when I ring you back. Now, tell me which of these two you want to go for?'

'Say again?' Even at this distance, Sarella felt her spirits lift—to be pitched back into the hurly-burly of her previous life was just the tonic she needed.

'Well, there's this sex romp with a social message. It'll run and run. Please your bank manager. Or there's the *Hamlet*.'

'Ophelia?'

'No, *Hamlet*, love. They're casting him as a woman. And they've got a nice young fellow to play Ophelia.'

'Sounds original.'

Beryl gave a chuckle. 'As your agent, I should advise you against it—my cut will be so minute that I'll lose it through a hole in my pocket. On the other hand, you sound as if you could do with a laugh. Tell you what, lovey, I'll play them both and see who bites first.'

As she rang off and Sarella was left holding the phone she thought she heard a click on the line as if somebody had replaced an extension. He wouldn't, she told herself. Maybe it was just a random noise long-distance.

Mildly cheered by this glimmer of light in the midst of nightmare, she made her way down to the library. There was sure to be a copy of *Hamlet* on the shelves. She wouldn't waste her enforced imprisonment in Castle Perilous, she would make a start on her lines! There was, she tried to tell herself, a bright side to everything.

She didn't catch sight of Marc until that afternoon. He was in the courtyard, unfastening a pair of skis, his jet-black ski-suit moulding itself to his body in a way that drew her glance whether she liked it or not. He looked tanned and fit. Even so, as he hoisted the skis over one shoulder and made towards the steps, she noticed the limp again. Somehow it made her heart ache with a wild mix of anguish and recrimination. Why did he have to hate her so much? What had she really done? He surely didn't expect Peter *never* to marry? Was he going to be like this towards every woman his younger brother brought home?

Thoughts of Peter etched a frown to her forehead. He hadn't contacted her since that early-morning call yesterday, and she wondered if he truly expected her to sit here, simply waiting for him like the princess in the tower.

Marc was stamping about at the top of the steps, knocking the snow off his boots. His face wore that concentrated look she had grown used to, as if everything he did was the focus of all his energies—like the look when he'd taken her in his arms and made his kiss seem the still point of the entire universe.

It means nothing, she told herself. He gives the same fierce concentration to the most trivial action. It's his way.

She was in the middle of Act Three when he came into the library. He didn't say anything and he didn't really look at her. Instead he went over to one of the shelves and pretended to be searching for a book. She tried to keep her attention on the lines, but they were already swimming off the page. Apparently finding what he wanted, he came over to the sofa on the other side of the low coffee-table that was all that stood between them, threw himself down among the cushions and started to read.

Five minutes elapsed. It was impossible. How was she supposed to concentrate with that sprawling figure almost in her line of vision? She re-read the previous page, but by the time she'd got to the bottom again it made as little sense as it had the first time. With a small exclamation she snapped the book shut, but before she could get to her feet Marc glanced up. Their eyes met.

'Going?'

Tight-lipped, Sarella merely nodded.

'Don't let me drive you away.'

'You're not.'

'Good.'

She gripped the book in both hands like a defensive weapon. 'You said we had to avoid each other.'

'I know.'

'So why don't you? I was here first.'

'I thought you'd had your fair share of the library.'

'Sorry.' She got to her feet.

'Sarella——' it was a breath of sound, but it acted like the most peremptory command, freezing her to the spot '—you don't have to go if you don't want to.'

'I can easily read upstairs.' She didn't move. She couldn't move, even though she wanted to—it was heaven and hell being close again, even if they were enemies and the minutes were flying by, bringing their separation ever closer.

'What are you reading?'

'A play,' she said grudgingly.

'What sort of play?'

'Shakespeare.'

'Which one?'

It was beginning to sound like an inquisition. Sarella jerked her head to look at him. '*Hamlet*,' she said. His eyes were piercing, bright as two pieces of jet, missing not a single thing as they moved inch by slow inch over her face.

'Why are you reading *Hamlet*?' he asked. 'Any particular reason?'

The memory of that click on the line came back. 'You know why,' she told him in a lemon voice.

'No, I don't.' He looked bemused.

'Don't lie,' she jerked out, going round behind the sofa, though not actually turning towards the door. She rested the book on a cushion. Her feet were like lead; she couldn't drag herself away. I want to see how long he'll go on denying the fact that he was listening in, she told herself to justify her inability to leave.

'I'm not lying. What is there to lie about?' He demanded, impassive as ever.

'I called my agent this morning.'

She paused and he raised his eyebrows as if inviting her to go on. When he said nothing she told him, 'You suggested it yourself. Of course, if you want me to pay for the call I will.'

'Don't be ridiculous.'

'I'd hate you to feel I was taking advantage of your hospitality.'

'Stop it. It's not like that—you know it isn't.'

'Isn't it?' She gave a hard laugh. Even now, when it would have been appropriate to leave the room, she couldn't tear herself away.

'It's not like that at all. There's a world of difference between a phone call connected with your work and a pair of my grandmother's pearl earrings.'

'I didn't know they were your grandmother's.'

'Peter did. He must have taken them back with him last time he was here.'

'He probably meant to ask you and forgot, knowing Peter.'

Marc's eyes opened a fraction wider and she saw something in his eyes that hadn't been there before. Then his lips tightened. 'When he shows up we can ask him, can't we?'

'If it bothers you. I shan't be here, so you can ask him what you like as far as I'm concerned.'

'He'll still be your fiancé, whether you're on the scene or not. You ought to show some interest.'

'I'm afraid my interest in the house of Vila has run its course. You can both go to hell for all I care,' Sarella wondered how it was they'd managed to get off the subject of the telephone call so quickly. Probably because for Marc it was dangerous ground. She jerked her chin at him. 'Don't think I'm ungrateful for being allowed to phone to the outside world,' she clipped, 'but you should have warned me that my conversation might be bugged. After all,' she went on, 'it might have been a private call—to a lover or someone.'

'Bugged? What do you mean?'

'Don't play dumb. You might be able to drive cars, but your acting doesn't convince.'

'I assure you, I'm not acting this time.'

'*This* time?' she exclaimed with a telling note of derision in her voice.

'I was acting the other times, yes.' He didn't look shamefaced; he seemed quite matter-of-fact.

Sarella recalled the smouldering look of desire in his eyes as he'd kissed her. He was *acting*—he had just said so. She felt as if she had been kicked in the stomach.

'You were testing me, seeing if I'd fit your image of that tarty little number who'd led your innocent younger brother astray?'

'You're saying all this.'

'Isn't that what you meant? You were acting because you wanted to see how far I'd go!' The copy of Shakespeare was being mutilated.

'It's true in a way. I'm sorry.'

'*Sorry?*' She couldn't believe her ears. 'You do a despicable thing like that, then calmly say you're *sorry?*'

Tears of pain and anger were crowding behind her eyelids.

'What do you want me to do, don sackcloth and ashes?'

'Do you sleep at night?' she hissed.

'Usually, though not so well of late.'

'I'm not surprised.'

'Not for the reasons you imagine, Sarella.' He offered her a bleak look, 'You're full of righteous indignation at the thought that I was cynically testing to see how far you'd go—but you offer no apology for your own behaviour. *And*,' he went on before she could interrupt, 'you can't deny you were all over me from the very beginning. I didn't have to do a thing. One touch and you forgot all about Peter. Wht sort of wife do you expect me to want for my brother? One who's going to cheat from day one?'

'Your concern for him is so touching. Now you're trying to say that you led me on out of *concern* for him——'

'Of course——'

'—But that's not the deal you offered later, is it?'

'I thought you might not balk at a straight proposition.' He didn't bat an eyelid.

'You're despicable.'

'I care too much about what happens to this family. But if I overstepped the mark it was because you made the running.'

'I?' Sarella went red. 'I didn't stand a chance! I tried to fight you off!'

'A token struggle.' He was emphatic.

'A *real* struggle.'

'I'm black and blue.'

She gave a low groan and brought one fist up to her forehead. 'I hate you. *I really hate you.*'

'We have already established that fact, for what it's worth.'

His voice was so dead, so cold, so indifferent to her that she could only stare at him with a block like concrete lodged somewhere near her heart. These weren't the words she wanted to hear from him. They weren't the words she was longing to speak. But what did she want? He was hateful. He despised her. He twisted everything she said and turned to nothing what she felt.

Swivelling, almost blinded by the plunging edifice of her emotions as he struck at their foundations, she groped towards the door. He didn't call her back, and when she turned he was sitting where she had left him, sprawled across the sofa surrounded by the solid things of his existence. *His* library, she listed, *his* home, *his* opinion, *his* power. Together they seemed to annihilate her. She stumbled away, broken and on the verge of despair.

That night was spent wrapped in a duvet, sitting on the windowsill in her room, gazing blindly out at the panorama of snow and ice below. Close to dawn she forced herself into bed, but she was still wide-eyed when the maid came in with an early-morning cup of tea.

'Is the road still impassable?' was the first question she asked.

When she nodded, Sarella turned her face to the pillow. Later, luckily by the time she was up and dressed, there was another knock on her door. 'Is your phone not working?' It was the same maid. Sarella glanced across at it. When she went to pick it up it was dead.

'There is a call. You may take it in Mr Vila's office,' said the maid. She led her downstairs along a corridor she had explored on her first day and indicated a door at the far end. When Sarella pushed it open she found herself in a sunlit room full of the latest office equipment. So this must be where Marc plots his business deals, she thought, trying not to show too much curiosity about the details flashing up on the several screens against the wall.

Marc presided behind a desk as big as a tennis court. He was in black—a thick high-necked sweater and, she noticed when he got up and came round the side of the desk, a pair of black corduroys that moulded his thighs as if tailored specially for him, as indeed they probably had been.

'Some of the lines are down,' he told her, sweeping her face without any expression on his own. 'Take it on that one over there.'

'Peter?' she asked as she went over to it.

He shrugged and shook his head as if he couldn't care less who it was. It was Beryl. 'OK, lovey,' she bellowed into the phone, 'when can you get back? I've fixed——' But there was a sound of static and her voice was cut off.

Sarella shook the phone. Nothing.

'Hell, has that gone too?' Marc reached out and took the receiver from between her fingers and spoke into it. He slammed it down into its cradle. 'Your agent?'

She nodded. It was lime and leather, she was thinking. She would never be able to bear the scent of either of them again.

'Fax her on the other line. You can use my number.'

'She wants to know when I'm going back.'

'She's got a job lined up for you?'

She nodded. 'Maybe.'

'What's the matter?' He peered into her face. 'You look pale.' A statement—there was no note of concern in his voice. The question was asked out of politeness only. 'Are you all right?' he insisted.

'Tired.'

'You look terrible.' His black eyes were expressionless.

'Thanks,' she said stiffly.

'You can't audition looking like that.'

'Why not? I might be playing Hamlet.' She gave an hysterical giggle. 'I'll walk it.'

'You won't if you don't get back to her,' he remarked without any inflection of interest.

'You're so efficient,' she replied, wishing for a moment that he could be on her side.

'That's another black mark, is it?' Something stirred in the depths.

'Not at all.' She half smiled. What was happening?

'You sounded like Peter for a minute.' His eyes were never leaving her face.

'Heaven forbid!' she exclaimed weakly.

Marc shot her a quick glance. 'You mean he's losing his allure.'

'It was never like that,' she couldn't help admitting.

'No?'

Sarella brushed a hand over her eyes. No—what a wealth of accusation in that one word! 'You've always known I wasn't in love with him.' As soon as she said it aloud she knew it was true. That was what his sharp intelligence had picked up from their first meeting.

'At last you admit it.' There was a reaction, quickly concealed, but whether of triumph or something else she couldn't discern.

'It's never come up before,' she pointed out, accurately enough.

'Hasn't it?' he intoned. 'I thought that was the major issue—your motive for getting engaged to him failing to be the normally accepted one of true love.'

'The issue for you was that you thought I was after his money. There is a difference between marrying someone while not loving them and marrying them in order to use them as a private bank.' It didn't matter what was said now. Her agent was talking somewhere on the air waves. Soon she would get through to her. Order would be re-established. 'How do I use your fax?' she asked to break the tension.

He went over to it and jerked his head impatiently when she didn't immediately follow him. She had to riffle through the pages of her notebook to find the number, which she had only rarely used. When she read it out to him he tapped it in for her. 'Go ahead,' he ordered.

Sarella paused with her fingers above the keys. 'I don't know what to say,' she admitted. 'When can I get away?'

'Arrange something for next week. That should give you ample time.'

He seems to have taken over, she thought, meekly doing as he suggested. On reflection she knew he was right. It seemed sensible to give herself time to readjust after she got back. He couldn't mean it would be another week before she left Rocamar.

'There,' she said, 'that's done.'

'Don't forget my number for her to call you back.' He tapped it in for her. 'What a team—we could go places.' He turned. 'So what is the difference?' he asked. 'Enlighten me.'

She tilted her face to his. 'You mean re Peter?'

'Re your reasons for getting engaged.'

'I——' She glanced down. After all that had happened she was still unable to betray Peter—in fact, it was because of all that had happened that she felt she couldn't be the one to give away the details of his difficulties, especially not to Marc, now that she knew how things stood between them both. It was for Peter to tell his brother the truth. Not her. 'He sort of talked me into it,' she said after a pause that seemed to have gone out of control. It sounded feeble. When she stole a glance to see how Marc was taking it his lips were white.

'He talked you into it?' he repeated heavily.

She nodded.

He didn't say anything, but she could imagine the ranging of his thoughts—how he himself had tried to talk her into something, though he couldn't know how she had stonewalled past the point where she knew what she was doing.

He lifted his dark head, turning, moving away from her. He went over to his desk and shuffled some papers. His movements seemed heavy, as if he were moving underwater. Something about the angle of his shoulders made her want to reach out to him. And she longed to feel him wrap his arms protectively around her again—she wanted to feel safe the way she had done in those brief moments on the terrace the other evening when for one miraculous instant she had believed there was something real between them.

She turned away. It was a delusion. Marc had already admitted he had been leading her on to see what she would do. Somehow it was hard to take in.

'Wait!'

She was already beside the door, and pivoted like someone in a dream in response to his call.

'Next week. . .' He seemed to lose the thread, then visibly pulled himself together. 'You won't get away for another day or two. While the snow's still good you may as well make use of it. I'm sure somebody can find you a pair of skis.' He gave a harsh laugh. 'No need to let Peter have all the fun.'

Sarella's head jerked in astonishment. 'You mean, go skiing?'

He nodded, his eyes pinpointing her expression as he

turned back to his work. 'Even Bluebeard has to have time off.'

She tried to smile, faint with the desire to stop the pretence. They were both behaving as if what they were saying was what was in their thoughts. 'After lunch, then,' she agreed.

'I'll find you.' Their eyes met. With a sickening reverberation the words stayed in her mind all the way back to her room. I'll find you. He made it sound as if there would never be any escape.

It was late afternoon and they were on their way back, swishing side by side through untouched snow down the last long sweeping run towards Rocamar. Contrary to what he had suggested, Marc was a good, fast skier, and it was Sarella who had had difficulty in keeping up. But then she hadn't expected it to be any different. He would be a world-champion tiddly-winks player too if he ever decided it was something worth taking up. She admired that trait in his character—just as she admired so many others.

They were skiing more slowly now, coming down the valley with Castell Rocamar like something out of a fairy-tale at its head. There were some trees below them, and when they reached them he slowed, she followed suit, and then he swished to a halt. She skidded on a little way, then side-slipped back towards him.

"You're looking less peaky,' he said as she came to a halt on the slope a few yards below.

'I feel really good!' she exclaimed. 'It's just what I needed to put things in perspective. You're lucky, Marc.' She glanced down the valley towards Rocamar. 'It's so gorgeous. Has it always been in your family?'

'You must be joking—we're the *arrivistes* round here. I told you, Father was based in Hong Kong. I bought this place when I was——' he frowned '—when I gave up motor racing. It's central for business, and,' he smiled, 'usually the lines of communication with the outside world are good enough.'

'It's a big place for one person—two,' she corrected, remembering how he had told her that it was Peter's home too.

'Suits me,' he replied shortly. 'Good for business.'

'Plenty of space to put people up.'

'That, yes.' His face looked drawn now that the flush of exertion from the last descent had left it.

'I'm surprised you didn't set up somewhere in a city,' she went on, tearing her glance from his face. 'Paris, Rome, Madrid.' A bachelor city, she was thinking. Somewhere where there was plenty of social life.

'I was thinking along the lines of a family home when I bought this,' he said abruptly. 'Ponies in the paddock, that sort of romantic scenario everyone has to come to terms with.'

'I see.'

'Do you?'

'I suppose so.' She bent to knock some snow from her bindings. He was using the past tense.

'Come on,' he said with an abrupt jerk, 'I'll race you to the bottom of the slope. It's a straight cruise to the drawbridge after that.'

Without time to do more than yell in protest as he set off, Sarella launched herself after him and did her utmost to keep pace. He was skiing like a demon and she came in a poor second.

'That wasn't fair!' she laughed as she skidded to a halt in the yard.

'You're pretty good—it was the only way I could be sure of winning!'

'Cheat!' For a moment all tension had gone.

'I only cheat to win!'

'That doesn't justify it!'

'Where did you learn anyway?' he asked as they snapped their skis off and bumped the ice from them before going in.

'On lots of winter holidays when I was a kid,' she told him. 'Both my parents were mad skiers. They made me learn almost before I could walk.'

'They sound OK.'

'They were.' Now it was she who was using the past tense.

He lifted an eyebrow.

'You don't miss a trick, do you?'

'Do you want me to?'

'No, it's all right. They were both killed in a car crash when I was sixteen.' She looked straight at him.

'Cars. So.' His lips were clamped in an unemotional line.

'Yes, well.' She gave a shrug, longing to acknowledge that they shared a sorrow, but unable to do so. She turned towards the steps. When he drew level she said, 'They left me a house and all the fruits of their labour. It means I can live in a good part of town in my own apartment. I've never had money worries. There's always been enough. Even in the year of provincial theatres.'

'I see.' He looked thoughtful.

'Do you? I would like to think so.' Now he knew she didn't need Peter's money. But that wasn't the point.

Strangely angry with him, Sarella pushed open the door and stamped inside. Snow fell off the bottom of her boots all over the tiled floor, but she didn't care. She clumped across the star-patterned mosaic towards the walk-in cupboard where the ski-gear was kept. When she was in her stockinged feet she moved to get out, but Marc was wedged in the doorway, unbuckling his boots.

He'd pulled the zip of his black ski-suit right down and she could see the fleecy red thermals he had on underneath. They were damp with sweat. The sight was unexpectedly erotic, making her imagine the heat of lovemaking. She found she couldn't tear her eyes away, and when he managed to get his second boot off and threw it to one side, then lifted his head, she was still staring. She gave a little shake of her head as if to pull herself back to reality.

But it was still unreal when he reached out and, bending over her, gently pushed back the wisps of hair that had loosened from beneath her headband.

The smell of waterproofs and leather was very strong in the confined space of the cloakroom, and it gave an unreal quality to everything. It was a moment separated from the normal flow of time.

Then he turned abruptly and, ducking his head under the lintel, went out into the hall. When she followed he was heading towards the kitchens. 'Come on, you deserve a glass of *Glühwein*.' He was brusque, as if the moment had never happened.

Confused, she went after him down the winding stairs into the kitchen and let him organise hot drinks. There were too many people about to maintain the level of intimacy that seemed to have taken them unawares jut now and, thankful that a further dilemma had been averted, she gratefully buried her face in her mug. The heady scent of hot spices restored the sense of relaxation that moment in the cloakroom had nearly undone. Confident that they were not going to start scratching each other's eyes out again, she drank deeply when Marc refilled her mug.

'It's been a perfect day,' she was forced to admit. 'I'm glad I spent it with you.'

'The feeling's mutual,' he replied rather stiffly, avoiding her glance. 'I'll be busy tomorrow. Maybe the day after we can think about getting you back down the mountain.'

The content of what he said might have chilled her if she had harboured any desire to stay longer—which, she told herself fiercely, she most definitely did not. Yet there was something in his tone that chilled her even more. It was the note of finality in his voice—it seared through her. Was this it? The end? But the end of what?

It was as if he were saying, 'There, I've done my duty as a good host. We don't like each other, but you can't fault my sense of hospitality. I've proved that, yes——' in the words he'd used that very morning '—even Bluebeard has to take time off. Now it's over.'

He'd charmed her and she'd succumbed once again.

That betraying look in her eyes in the cloakroom just now must have told him he'd won again.

Miserably Sarella replaced her empty mug on the table and got up. 'I'd better go and look over the script before dinner,' she told him without meeting his eyes. She made her escape without another word.

CHAPTER SEVEN

IN VIEW of what Marc had said about the next few days, Sarella was surprised when he sought her out before dinner. She had just slipped into a black taffeta skirt and was buttoning the front of her blouse when there was a knock on the door. Thinking it was probably one of the maids, she hastily did up the last button and went to open it.

'Hi.' He was draped in the doorway, sporting a chunky oatmeal sweater and a pair of thigh-hugging beige trousers and looking tanned and fit after their afternoon in the snow.

'I'm ravenous after all that exercise,' he announced, allowing his glance to flicker over the hastily buttoned blouse. He noticed the flattering knee-length skirt and the black stockings and gave a smile. 'How about starting dinner early?' And when she hesitated he went on, 'I've got an uncut film version of *Hamlet* you might like to run. Researching your part? We could watch it after we've eaten, but if you'd like to see it we'll need to make an early start.'

Sarella didn't hesitate. 'You must be hungry if you're promising to sit through Shakespeare afterwards!'

'It's the Russian version. Subtitled.'

'You're famished!' She glanced back into the room. There was no need to take anything with her. She wasn't going far. Switching off the light, she followed Marc downstairs. Even during their teasing exchange his eyes had seemed to be giving another message, trailing over her lips and, briefly, to the V of her blouse. But, she reminded herself, he still despised her because she was a fortune-hunter who had conned the family jewels from his innocent kid brother. . .Warning herself to tread carefully this evening, she followed him into the dining-room.

'Not here,' he informed her, beginning to stride across the echoing expanse of the refectory with her close on his heels. 'I really only use this place when there are a lot of guests, and for balls and that sort of thing. Fulfilling my seigneurial duties!' He laughed, mocking himself. 'We'll eat in the breakfast-room. There should be a fire in there.'

He was right. Logs were ablaze in the wide hearth and the air was aromatic with the smell of pine. It made it a cosy scene, an effect enhanced by the glow of several candles placed in tall sconces against the wall. There was a smaller group of candles in the middle of the table too, but, she noticed, this time there was no accompanying rose. There was something else, though.

As she took her place she noticed a piece of paper by the side of her plate. With a puzzled lift of her head she found he was watching her with a faraway expression in his eyes. 'What is it?' she asked, picking it up.

'Read it.'

'Oh, it's a reply to my fax from Beryl!'she exclaimed as she scanned the first paragraph. 'But that's wonderful!' Her grip tightened on the flimsy sheet. 'Isn't that wonderful?' She lifted her head.

'Congratulations. Which will you choose?'

'I can't believe it. . .definitely the *Hamlet* if I want it—I've worked with those people before; remember I told you about the provincial-theatre year?' she said, scrambling her words. 'And an audition on the twelfth for what Beryl calls the sex romp with political overtones, whatever that means. Oh, she is a card! You'd love her, she's completely mad——!' She bit her lip. What was she saying? Rabbiting on as if—as if they were friends at the very least. . .

He didn't appear to notice the way her words suddenly tailed away. 'Would you celebrate if you were at home?' he was asking with that same faraway look in his eyes.

'Not until the contracts were signed and sealed. I wouldn't dare!' Sarella smiled happily, pushing her other feelings aside and admitting, 'I'm superstitious when it comes to work. Better to be safe than sorry. And never count your chickens. That's what Mother always used to say.' Her eyes clouded briefly. 'She would be so pleased, you know. She was an actress herself before she married. Dad wasn't in the business and I think she used to miss it.' She frowned. 'Beryl calls herself my stand-in mum.' She was re-reading the last line of the message which hadn't sunk in till now. 'Who's the Voice?' it said. 'I'll audition *him* any time!'

She looked up and bit her lip, knowing Marc could tell she had just read it.

He switched on the powerhouse smile. 'She sounds a real character. *Do* you need a stand-in?'

She nodded. 'It's good to know she's there—not having any family of my own.' Conversation was somehow easier after that—Beryl's news gave them something neutral to talk about. Sarella herself was buoyed up by the thought that soon this nightmare would be over and she would be able to pull herself together under cover of a solid stint of hard work. The lead in *Hamlet* was enough to take her mind off anything.

'We haven't heard from Peter today,' Marc pointed out after the conversation eventually veered away from theatrical things. 'What did he tell you he was going to do?'

Fearing dangerous ground, Sarella glanced away. 'He

told me he would get back as soon as the roads were clear.'

'What's he really doing over there?'

She shook her head. 'I assumed he was going to the apartment to pick up some papers,' she said vaguely. She darted a glance across the table and coloured when she saw the piercing intelligence in his dark eyes.

'When are you going to level with me, Sarella?' he asked lightly.

She tried to pretend she didn't know what he meant, but his bantering tone had been deceptive. He leaned forward.

'I know it's difficult for you, living in a world of make-believe as you obviously do. But I'm not a fool and I object to being thought one. It's obvious Peter has got himself into money difficulties and hit on the idea of producing a fiancée in order to get his hands on his share as the quickest way of solving them. Whether you yourself knew this or not is immaterial. Obviously he would promise to make it worth your while. That's between the two of you. Though——' he sat back and gave her a grim smile '—I hope he's not such a fool as to pay over the odds for your services.'

Sarella's breath was knocked out of her. Here she was, imagining that the last half-hour had been a sort of truce—telling Marc all those things about her life on the stage, all those silly, funny, self-mocking stories of disaster and mayhem that were part of the business, and he'd been sitting there in judgement all that time, working out how much Peter might or might not have paid her for playing the part of his fiancée. . .

Forcing her voice through frozen lips, she hid her inner turmoil and quipped, 'You make being engaged to Peter sound like just another job!'

'Isn't that exactly what it's been? Another professional

engagement? You admit you don't love him. You simply signed the contract and did the job.' His eyes glinted. 'Quite well too. Apart from one or two lapses, you've been a model of fidelity.' He went on, 'I can't really understand why. I'm sure he didn't expect you to play the part to the hilt. I'm sure he's not doing likewise.'

'So you tried to suggest before,' she replied, 'and, as I said then, he's a free agent.'

'So why the reluctance to follow suit?'

Her heart was pounding and, realising there was no point in pretending any longer, she opted for frankness, saying, 'It would only be lust.' She paused, then added without inflection, 'Wouldn't it?'

They had both become very still. When Marc spoke it was on another topic altogether. 'If you want to run that video and get to bed before daybreak we'd better go down now.'

Taking care with her napkin, Sarella folded it into eight equal parts. By the time she followed him he was already halfway across the barren, mirrored expanse of the room beyond and her features were carefully arranged to hide every vestige of the heartbreak underneath.

They sat together like an old married couple in separate armchairs facing the screen. It was a film made some years ago in black and white, but, despite the difficulty of watching it in a foreign language, the power of the drama gripped them both, Sarella because she was a professional and was impressed by the intensity of the acting, and Marc because it seemed to strike some deep chord within him. After the final tragic scene he leaned back and closed his eyes.

It was after midnight. She was conscious of the silent

castle rooms enclosing them, and beyond them the outer
walls, and beyond those the barren miles of frozen
snow.

'Any use to you?' he asked, snapping open his eyes as
he heard the rustle of her skirt as she changed position.

She sighed. 'It was brilliant. I can't see how I can
bring anything fresh to it.' She pondered for a moment.
His eyes were still on her, and in an attempt to restore
the illusion of chumminess they had built up during
dinner she went on, 'I wonder what the actor playing
Ophelia will make of it? I mean, she's rejected by the
man she loves and drowns herself rather than live
without him. He'll find that difficult, I should think—
when men are losers in love they tend to react
differently.'

'How do you mean?' He raised his eyebrows.

'Well, they become violent, don't they? Or they
pretend they don't care.' Her eyes suddenly met his.

To her surprise he jerked to his feet and went over to
the video machine and yanked the cassette out without
rewinding it. Dropping it noisily back into its box, he
replaced it on the shelf. She was hurt, though not
surprised, by his ability to switch off as soon as she
wanted to talk. It was as if she had said something and it
had caused a click in his mind that brought down the
shutters to keep her out.

Casting her mind back, she tried to work out what it
was, piecing together what she knew of him. For some
reason she recalled that moment during the afternoon
when they had stood together on the slope looking down
on Rocamar.

The place had been intended as a family home, he had
told her. Then he had simply skied off like a maniac—
anger, she registered. He must have been trying to hide
the feelings that the sight of Rocamar conjured up, for

he himself had dubbed it a romantic dream—and the dream had failed.

Then she remembered Peter telling her how much his brother liked women—and how much they liked him. He hadn't mentioned anyone special. But it didn't take a genius to guess there had been a woman involved, someone with whom to share the dream of Rocamar. Her memory must be lingering in every lonely room and courtyard—hence his hardness now. His unforgiving attitude to what he saw as infidelity. His ability to feel nothing, despite the superficial passion of his kisses.

He was still shuffling videos on the shelves as if having suddenly noticed that someone—herself, probably—had replaced them in the wrong order.

Her heart was like lead. There were no photographs around, but what a fool she was to imagine that the expression in his eyes meant more than the harsh words he dealt her. There wasn't one word of commendation in anything he had ever said to her. That was proof conclusive for anyone but the blindest of fools.

Weary now that the excitement of the film was no longer sweeping her along, she pulled herself to her feet. Marc had finished his rearrangement of the videos and moved across the room just as she herself moved forward. They came face to face on the rug between the two chairs.

Shock waves of desire flashed through her form before she could stop them. She turned to escape. He sidestepped to let her pass and they collided. He put out an arm and dropped it as soon as it touched her, as if its contact stung him. 'Your eyes are enormous,' he announced hoarsely. 'Are you tired?'

Her mouth opened and closed. Swooping patterns of energy tingled down the labyrinths of her nerves. He raised his hand and placed it on her arm where it had briefly touched before. This time he let it stay.

In thickening tones he demanded, 'So what's so bad about lust?'

She felt powerless as he brought up his other hand and let his fingers feather lightly down the side of her neck to her collar-bone. There they rested before continuing in a slow trickle of delicious sensation to the neck of her blouse.

She tried to make a movement of resistance, but it only seemed to aid the passage of his touch. His fingers slid on their taunting trail lower and yet lower still until she was ready to scream with the command to stop.

But she was transfixed. What was so bad about lust? she asked herself. Except that for her it wasn't lust at all. But she was already locked within the power of his desire, within the focus of that concentrated attention that had held her in thrall before.

Three fingers whispered against the skin in the V of her blouse, reaching inside to move within the lace edge of her bra, pushing beneath the confinement of it with greater insistence, hot now and seeking more intimacy than that first feather-light touch had allowed. With a gasp she felt his palm close firmly round one of her breasts, circling and squeezing until she felt her nipples harden and an explosion of fire sweep through her entire body, sending her head back, lips opening, lids heavy and breath deepening uncontrollably as her arms came up around his neck.

Somehow his other hand had slipped inside the back of her waistband and begun to mould her buttocks in firm strokes that matched her pelvis against his own, energising her desire with the heat of his own ardent body. Conscious of a ripping sound, she heard her zip go, then her taffeta skirt was rustling to the floor and he was pulling her down among its glossy folds, his lips marauding over hers so that it was the way it was in the unrequited dreams of the empty nights when everything came down to the touch of him like the still centre of the entire world.

Now he was in earnest about making her his possession, his unpent desire overriding any token resistance she might have made. Her fear at what was about to happen assumed the image of one black ogre, defeated instantly by the joy of feeling the strength of his body against hers, conscious of the sureness, the confidence, the single-mindedness of his wanting. His certainty made her feel safe. She could give herself to him. He desired her, no one but her. And in the delirium of recognising her power she felt protected, safe in his arms.

His lips were doing wonderful things to one of her ears and she heard him swallow, then rasp, 'I'm taking you upstairs to my room.'

He knelt over her for a moment, tough and handsome in the candlelight, his eyes triumphant with the knowledge of desire on the verge of fulfilment, possessing her as only he could, then he was bending, lifting her into his arms, carrying her across the room, and she felt the sudden chill as the door opened and, wedging it awkwardly with his foot, he bundled her through it.

Aware only of the bumping of her heart and the pressuring of his mouth on hers even as he carried her through interminable pathways to the journey's end, Sarella felt him lower her at last on to his bed. Now another journey began, one of which she had no memory, no knowledge of the decision to start, but one which she was made powerless by love to turn from.

His swiftly naked body was somehow beside her and over her, and then sharply, at first painfully, then joyfully within her, and she cried his name aloud with the voice of the woman that had been lying buried within her all her life. After that first shock of entry she had offered herself without shame, but Marc had slowed, holding her wildness in check, and with a hoarse, inquisitorial, 'Sarella?' had tried to hold them back upon their course. But as she moved instinctively beneath him he buried his face in her hair with a groan and then plunged into the very flower of her being.

Wider and wider yet spread the waves of ecstasy, fooling her into believing that the limit had been reached, then carrying her on further into a boundless realm. When she arched finally, feeling him convulse with a groan between joy and pain, she was swept by waves of pride at the gift that had been given and received, her fingers pulling at the thick dark hair, pushing possessively over the muscles of his back, sliding down the sweat-soaked hollows of his spine to the tight muscles slackening in the aftermath of love.

He enveloped her mouth in one last, languid taking, then rolled on to the pillow beside her. 'I feel,' he said, 'as if I've been waiting a hundred years for you.'

. He lifted one arm across her, paralleling her own, spreading it out over the double bed above her head until their fingers meshed. She could feel him find the ring on her third finger, the one Peter had found in the snow one day and thrown across the shop counter to her when nobody had come to claim it. Marc slid it off and trailed it all the way back along her inner arm as he withdrew his own. He stroked the side of her face with it, amused by her attempts to catch his fingers in her teeth, teasing her with it, darting little touches here and there on her lips. She caught the ring at last between her teeth and he tickled her until she laughed and gave it up. Then he capped his own little finger with it and held it up for them both to see. 'And it wasn't even consummated,' he observed sardonically. He glanced down at her flushed face in its frame of wild hair. The expression in the dark eyes was ambivalent. 'What did you tell him to keep him away?'

She was sinking down into a dream, aware only of the warmth of his body wrapped intimately against her own. Turning her head, she pressed her lips against the unfamiliar contours of his chest, triumphing gently in the textures and definition of a perfect body.

'Sarella?' he murmured, shifting his weight a little to enable her to continue her first tentative exploration. 'You can tell me now.'

'Nothing,' she said. 'I've always told you it wasn't like that.'

'Is he a loser or what?' He shifted again and gave a groan. 'Imagine leaving you behind without showing you what was what!' He shifted again, urging her to greater daring as her mouth continued its explorations. 'I could never have taken your word for it. . . Don't stop,' he commanded huskily as she lifted her head.

'You're so lovely,' she said, not listening to him but sliding her hands hungrily down his flanks. 'So perfect. So heavenly.'

'Don't say any more—I'll get conceited!' He rumpled her hair, holding her head between both hands as she rubbed her cheeks more feverishly over his flat stomach. The muscles were taut, a perfect symmetry, with a line of dark hair leading to the darker mystery she had yet to explore. Everything was new to her, magical, mysterious. Marc was her toy. Her god. Her love.

'You're so lovely,' she murmured again and again. He held her head more tightly as her lips discovered more secrets. She was crying now, greedy for him again, desperate for something she did not understand. Suddenly it wasn't enough. She was empty. There was no way she knew to fill up the violent sadness that had emptied her. Then he was pulling her down over him, turning her in his arms, twining her limbs around his own, filling up her emptiness, tending her craving with all the knowledge he possessed.

Sarella had never faced the awkwardness of the morning after, the problem of form—who should get up first, go to the bathroom first, offer the first kiss. Until now it had been outside her experience. . .

She lay as if drugged by love, problems such as these far from her conscious mind. Marc's beautiful bronze limbs weighted her down, and she squirmed surreptitiously without waking him in order to change her position so that she could look at him properly.

Her glance flitted lovingly over his sleeping face. All night they had loved each other, possessively, greedily, and she had been—still was—his slave in love.

All the problems that had beset them from that first moment their eyes had met in the courtyard on the day of her arrival had vanished, it seemed, giving way to the greater power of one fact—now they were lovers.

The first harbinger of the outside world came when the bedroom door suddenly opened and a maid came in with a tray. Marc murmured something and turned over, and Sarella sat up with a gasp of embarrassment.

The maid's expression didn't alter. 'I'll go and get another cup.' That was all she said before going out.

'Marc! Wake up. . .She saw me!'

'Mm?' He lifted one arm and groped heavily to wedge her firmly against his side.

'Stop it, Marc! Your maid came in!'

'Doesn't matter.' He was waking up, trying to drag

her back under the covers. She resisted for no more than a second, then joined him in the secret dark underneath. 'She didn't seem surprised,' she accused.

'Only doing her job. . .' he muttered. 'Come here and do yours.'

'What. . .? No, Marc. . .' Vainly she tried to pull away, but he was crushing her beneath his superior weight. 'You're a terrible man——' she managed to croak as he touched her in a way that transported her back at once to the heaven of the previous night.

'Let's stay here all day,' he suggested later. 'No point in getting up. You can't go anywhere.'

'I don't want to go anywhere,' she murmured, sucking the ends of his fingers under the covers. Her little ring had gone. They had discovered it in the bed last night when one of them had found themselves lying on it, and it had been pitched out into the darkness. 'I want to stay here forever with you. . .'

'Debauched little madam, what am I going to do with you?' he teased, and in a few minutes had shown her very definitely what possibilities he had in mind. There was no limit to his imagination, and she was his slavishly willing pupil. After that she must have fallen asleep, for when she next came round he had gone.

When he hadn't returned within half a hour Sarella sat up, shaking her head to clear it and looking round his room with gentle eyes. It was a four-poster bed, like the one in the guest-room—that much she had realised during the night—but the room itself was bigger, with a balcony beyond double french doors with pots of geraniums on it. There was a fireplace too with a large fur rug in front of it, and she fantasised about making love there in the blaze of the log fire with the snow beating like feathers against the windows.

She got up and went to look outside. There was a blue

sky this morning and a dripping sound, which she located as the sound of melting snow, pattering from the eaves. Previously it had been the sound she'd longed to hear, but now it filled her heart with music in a minor key, for it was a sound like the drip of tears. It was as if the castle were weeping.

Puzzled to find her thoughts taking such a melancholy turn when she felt so wonderful inside, Sarella made her way into the bathroom and ran a shower. She would wash her hair. Marc came in as she was towelling it dry.

'Going already?' He prowled over to her, arms reaching to fold her possessively within their sheltering curve. She had to stand on tiptoe to reach his lips.

He pushed her away with a groan of regret. 'We're going to have a visitor,' he informed her. 'Are you going to receive him in bed like an empress or downstairs in the drawing-room like an innocent?'

'Peter?' she guessed.

'He pushed a fax through some time last night. He should be arriving any time.' Marc gave her an odd look. 'I have things to see to in my office.' He turned to go, then told her what she knew already. 'The thaw's started.'

After he'd gone she borrowed his bathrobe and made her way back to her own room to dress. There was a peculiar lowering of her spirits, the cause of which she failed to pin-point. She put it down to the dismal sound of the thaw.

They were standing on the terrace just before lunch, watching the shrinking white mantle that had covered the slopes for the last two days, when a dark shape moving fast appeared further up the valley. It was heading towards the castle, and as it came nearer she saw it was a skier.

'Peter,' observed Marc, following the direction of her gaze. 'Trust him to turn up on skis!' He spoke with a fondness that was quickly stifled.

They watched in silence until he came closer, then, as he swooped between the grey walls of the drawbridge and came clattering into the courtyard over cobblestones that were now covered only by a thin film of slush, Marc deliberately removed his arm from around her waist. 'Tell him without delay,' he said, scarcely moving his lips. 'I don't like deception.'

He leaned over the balcony and called down, 'Good run?'

'Brilliant!' Peter's face was glowing as he turned to look up. 'I told you I'd be back today!'

'You've only just made it before the final melt.' Marc turned to Sarella and lifted one eyebrow as if to convey some more significant meaning. Her face must have registered dismay at having to tell Peter what had happened, for he gave a narrow smile. 'Pigeons always come home to roost, my dear.'

'Marc. . .' She put out a hand and touched him on the sleeve, but he moved back as if he hadn't noticed, and she said on a rising note, 'Why are you looking like that?' And when he merely swept one cold glance over her face she lurched forward, grabbing at his sleeve, holding on, asking, 'What are you thinking? You know how it is between us. Why are you looking like that?'

'I said tell him straight away. It's your job—though if you balk at it I'll do it.'

'Of—of course I'm going to tell him,' she stammered. Somehow she had imagined them both greeting Peter together, wrapped in each other's arms, confirming what Peter had already imagined when he'd rung her the other morning. There would have been no need for the clumsy intervention of verbal explanations.

But Marc had put down the shutters again.

Sarella looked down into the courtyard where Peter was busily taking off his skis. He was no doubt already anticipating some such development. His familiarity with his brother's behaviour would be based on past form, something she hadn't wanted to dwell on, for surely it had been different this time? Last night's lovemaking had changed everything for Sarella herself; she had never guessed it could be like that, and she couldn't imagine that it might not have been as earth-shattering for Marc too.

But why was he looking at her now with no sign of warmth in his glance? Hadn't it meant the same for him? It was almost as if he didn't want to have anything to do with her. He was even removing her fingers from his arm with every sign of impatience.

'I'll leave you to greet him alone. Tell him I shall be in my office. OK?' With a dismissive jerk of the head he went back inside.

Sarella leaned over the balustrade and waited while Peter seemed to take an age to come in. Unable to bear the suspense, she hurried down into the hall. He was half in and half out of the cloakroom, stripping off his ski-suit, jumping about on one leg with his other foot caught in the elasticated cuff. She couldn't help smiling.

'Want a hand?' she asked, coming up behind him.

He turned with a grin. 'Great—just keep still.' He held on to her shoulder while he disentangled himself. 'That's better.' He grinned down at her. 'Aren't you pleased with me? I told you I'd get back. You see, you *can* trust me, after all.'

'You're looking remarkably pleased with yourself——' Sarella began.

'So would you if you'd covered the length of the valley

in. . .' he flicked a glance at his wrist-watch '. . .seventy-four minutes precisely.'

'Good going. But is that all you have to tell me?'

He put both arms round her shoulders and looked down into her face with a wide grin. 'You're looking great. Different somehow. More tousled.' He ran both hands up into the roots of her hair, which she happened to be wearing down, and tried to plant a kiss on her forehead.

'*Peter*!' It was Marc's voice, cutting through the air like a whiplash.

Peter turned, one arm casually draped over Sarella's shoulders, and greeted Marc with a cheerful wave. 'Come on, admit you're impressed!' he coaxed. 'Do I get the Vila Trophy for valley-skiing or not?'

Marc was not amused. 'Has Sarella spoken to you?' His glance moved between the two of them. 'You'd better come and listen to what I have to say. I shall be in my office.'

'Oh, hell, give me a chance!' protested Peter, hanging more tightly on to Sarella's shoulders. 'Don't I get a chance to have a quiet few minutes with poor old Sarella?' Turning, he kissed her on the forehead.

Sarella tried to break away. Marc's dark eyes were boring soullessly into hers. 'Peter,' she said desperately, 'I think you should know——' She bit her lip. Why didn't Marc go away and leave it to her as he'd suggested, if that was what he wanted? It would be far easier than if he was just going to stand over her like a portent of doom with that horrible expression on his face. It was like the first time she'd seen him, just after Peter had introduced her as his fiancée. But now there was no need for it, surely? He knew the truth. No one was trying to deceive anyone else.

'Peter,' she began again, 'can we go into the sitting-room? I have something to say.'

'We both have things to say,' he told her with a fond smile. More quietly he added, 'Don't worry, you're off the hook. Everything's going to be all right.'

Marc had swivelled, his face satanic, both brows drawn together in one forbidding line.

'What's up with him? Have you two been at logger-heads all the time I've been away?'

'Not exactly.'

Something in her manner must have got through to him, for when she turned abruptly towards the sitting-room without another word he followed her, his face clouding. 'OK,' he began as soon as he had closed the door. 'Something's happened, hasn't it?'

She nodded, unsure how to go on.

'Marc?' he said, turning towards the window. 'And you?' He spun to catch the conflicting expressions crossing her face. 'It's all right, love, I know what he's like. I guessed you'd fall head over heels for him. Women always do. And, let's face it, you're more of a pair than we two are. It was at the back of my mind all along, you and him. I thought, once I'm sorted out—well, I knew there would be no future for us. I felt you'd both hit it off. You're alike, somehow.'

'I'm sorry, Peter. My feelings seem to have taken over. Somehow it seemed right. . . It's just. . .' Sarella furrowed her brow. 'I don't know. . . Now I feel terrible. . .' She couldn't forget Marc's expression just now.

'Life has a habit of changing the rules,' Peter shrugged. 'Don't worry on my account. I told you—it was at the back of my mind all along. You suit each other. The perfect couple.' He laughed. 'But for your sake I only hope you're not in it too deeply.'

'What do you mean?'

He shifted uncomfortably and tried to give her a reassuring grin. 'Oh, you know,' he replied vaguely. 'Love 'em, leave 'em. Marc's changed a lot in the last three years. He's harder.'

'Since the accident?' she probed.

'And the rest.'

She tilted her head.

'Woman trouble,' he added darkly. He strode briskly over to her and took her in his arms. 'Stop looking so stricken,' he murmured. 'You're still my best friend. Am I still yours?'

CHAPTER EIGHT

'PETER,' said Sarella when she'd got over the shock of
what he'd just said, 'surely you don't imagine we can go
on with this charade any longer?' When he didn't reply
she hurried on, 'There's not a chance he's going to accept
it. He's not a fool. He knew from the start we didn't love
each other. You deceived me completely, didn't you?
You said, "let's pretend to be engaged to tease big
brother", and you made it somehow seem as if it was a
sudden whim. But you must have thought of it already
when you invited me up here. You didn't warn me what
was at stake. You didn't even give me a chance to say I
wouldn't do it. I realise now it was all solely to get those
debtors off your back. . .' She faltered, unsure how to
continue.

'Are you saying you want out? Now?' He gripped her
by both shoulders. 'You can't back out just yet, Sarella—
please! It would be worse than useless. He's got to go to
those trustees and let them know I'm capable of handling
my own money.'

'But you're not, Peter. Face facts!' she burst out. 'You
know Marc better than I do, and you should have
realised he's not a fool. I've already told you he knew the
minute he saw us that there was something wrong——'

'And now you're trying to tell me you told him
everything?'

'No, of course not. I promised. And anyway,' she said
heatedly, 'it's obvious I don't know the whole story. And
one thing's sure; Marc's guessed there's some problem

over money. He's not stupid!' She pushed him away. 'Why did you drag me into this?'

'Because you like me and I like you, and you're my friend and I know I can trust you.'

'That's emotional blackmail!'

'I know. I'm sorry. But it also happens to be true. Who else can I trust? There's a lot at stake, and when you know the full story you won't be so hard on me.' Peter gazed out of the window as if steeling himself to make a confession. Sarella's heart was wrung for a moment as she remembered how hard Marc was on his younger brother. Perhaps there were good reasons for trying to outwit him in this way? How could she judge him when she didn't know the facts?

He turned to her. 'I do love you, Sarella—in a sort of brotherly way.' He looked abashed. 'That's not a lie. Of course, marriage is impossible, and, anyway, it's the last thing you'd want. I'm afraid I'm not a very serious person. Not like Marc. I'm sorry. I shouldn't have used you like this. I didn't mean it in the cold-blooded way it seems to have turned out.' He came towards her and put both hands on her shoulders. His eyes were without guile. 'I'm glad you let me sweep you along.'

'It's a common failing of Sarella's, it seems.'

She spun round to see Marc standing in the doorway. Peter's hands slid from her shoulders.

'It seems you can be swept along by almost anyone. Especially, I suspect, when there's something vital at stake, like a small fortune, for instance.'

'No!' she gasped. 'That's not true——'

'Look here!' exclaimed Peter at the same moment.

Marc fished in his pocket and held something out to them.

'So?' blustered Peter. 'Sure I gave them her. I thought they'd look pretty——'

Marc was holding out the Regency earrings. His dark eyes swept Sarella's face with contempt. '*Pretty?*' he demanded. 'Thirty-thousand pounds' worth of prettiness?'

'Isn't she worth it?' Peter put an arm round her shoulder and, despite her resistance, pulled her against him. 'Come on, Marc, unbend a little. You're lucky I didn't sell the damned things. She's a darling, she deserves nice things, and you know full well she did it all for——' He paused.

'Well, not *love*, that's for sure,' cut in Marc at once. His glance zipped from one to the other. 'I assume you made it worth her while in other ways, but obviously I failed to discover from her own fair lips how much you thought she was worth, and I'm damned sure you won't admit how much you've paid over the odds for her favours.' He smiled thinly. 'Though after last night. . .' his glance raked her face '. . .maybe you'd have done quite well out of the deal if you'd bothered to follow through.'

Sarella felt Peter's grip tighten protectively, and if it hadn't she was positive she would have crumpled under this attack. Her eyes swam and she put out a hand as if to ward off the blows.

'Steady on, Marc! You're talking about my best friend, not about some——'

'Forget her for a minute if you can,' snarled Marc. 'Why didn't you tell me you'd taken the pearls? Did you intend them as a short-term loan, retrievable when your contract with Sarella was over, or was it more in the line of outright theft? You know they're not yours.'

'They belong to the family. I was under the impression that we shared certain things equally. And,' he went on, before Marc could interrupt, 'you happened to be in Paris when I came over for them. I admit I should have left a message, but I assumed I would be seeing you shortly, and—hell, I never expected you to mind. What use are pearl earrings to you? I can't imagine you wanting to decorate any of your lady friends in pearls after what happened last——'

Marc's face was suffused with colour and he took a violent step forward. It was enough to stop Peter in mid-sentence. Sarella felt him stiffen as if expecting his brother's anger to turn to blows, but Marc went on rapidly, 'Why can't any of us talk without it turning into a slanging match? You've explained your position so far as the earrings go, Peter, and I accept your explanation, though I can't say I find it good enough. At least I can only be thankful you didn't think of pawning them. However, that's all in the past. Now I want you to tell me the important part—why the hell are you so desperate that you'll go to this extent in order to get your hands on the bequest? You've never been kept short of money, have you?'

Peter released his grip on Sarella and stepped forward. 'One,' he said, 'I'm legally of age to conduct my life as I wish. Two, if I decide I want to marry ten times over what the hell's it got to do with you?'

She felt Marc's eyes come to rest on her.

'Any port in a storm?' he asked coolly. 'There are any number of young girls you can marry if you wanted to—I mean properly, not as a farrago of the real thing.'

'Sarella understands me.'

'Yes?'

'*Yes.*' Peter put his hands in his pockets.

'You surely don't see it continuing down the years?' Marc's voice dripped with disbelief.

'If I'd got engaged to anybody else, any of these young girls you cite, they'd expect things from me I'm not prepared to give——'

Marc raised his eyebrows at this.

Peter laughed. 'Don't worry, nothing dreadful. I manage to function quite normally. It's just——' here he shot a glance at Sarella '—my heart happens to be engaged elsewhere.'

'So, damn it, why not marry elsewhere?'

'Because,' said Peter carefully, still looking at Sarella, 'there are problems.'

Her eyes widened. France, she thought. There's someone in Fance. Oh, why won't he tell the truth?

'What sort of problems?' asked Marc testily.

'Mind your own damn business,' Peter replied at once. 'I wouldn't expect a sympathetic hearing from you, anyway.' Sarella's heart plunged.

Marc gave him a level glance. 'You may as well tell me the lot.'

'Why? What difference is it going to make?'

'You can't go on pretending Sarella and you are serious. There's no point in it. I'm not going to advise the trustees to release the inheritance even if you do continue, so you may as well get rid of her. There are grounds.'

'You can't stop them.'

'Can't I just!'

'So we'll fight over it.' Peter turned to Sarella. 'You'll stand by me, won't you, love?'

She lifted stricken eyes to his. 'Oh, Peter——'

'Keep out of this,' broke in Marc. 'The last two days have shown you have no place whatsoever in this family.'

'What do you mean?' She turned in confusion, vainly trying to make sense of his animosity.

'He was gone two days and you finish up——' He smiled without humour. 'Need I go into details? All I can say is——' he bowed his hand '—*thank you, ma'am.*'

Sarella's sharp intake of breath brought Peter to her

side with one arm coming round her. 'You've turned into some sort of monster since Suzanna left you,' he said shortly. 'If you think you're going to make me treat Sarella in the same sort of way you're mistaken. She's worth a hundred of a woman like Suzanna, and if you can't see the difference you're a fool!'

Marc looked merely bored by this. 'The trustees are very old friends of mine and they're men of the world. They won't wear it for one minute when I tell them the whole story.'

'You don't *know* the whole story!'

'I will, don't worry.' Marc gave a hard laugh. 'The fact is, my dear boy, you've entered into a liaison with a woman who is totally unsuitable on every count.' He paused. 'She plays for higher stakes than the ones you can offer.' He laughed again. 'At least there's something rather apt about what happened last night. It was probably the custom for the owner of Rocamar to exercise his seigneurial rights over his guests in the good old days.'

Peter held on to Sarella as she gave a little cry and lurched forward. She shook off his restraining arm.

'Why are you doing this?' she cried.

'Because you've both deceived me. You, my dear, thought you were being particularly clever. As I said the morning of Peter's departure, when the cat's away the mice will play. You thought you'd play—for higher stakes than those he was offering. Why go for the chorus when you can have the starring role? You made it plain from the moment you met me that you were available, but you miscalculated if you imagined I'd fallen for your little scheme.'

'But——' Sarella shut her eyes. The nightmare was closing in. 'It never occurred to me to think of you like that,' she whispered.

'You made several mistakes,' he went on brutally. 'The most glaring one was last night when you tried to appeal to my pragmatic nature by admitting that "it would only be lust"—no doubt you imagined we could establish some sort of "adult" agreement on the basis of that.' His laugh was harsh. 'My standards are somewhat different. "Only lust" doesn't have any appeal for me these days.'

'But I didn't mean—I meant——' She floundered in a sea of confusion, not sure now, in the face of his implacable logic, what she did mean. Then she gathered her wits. 'I meant, it was only lust for you—not that I——' It didn't seem to make any more sense this way. He was gazing through her, black eyes like two probes, annihilating her with his immovable hostility.

Peter was somehow taking her into his arms, hissing something in Marc's face, but she couldn't tell what. Then together she and Peter were helping each other from the room, Marc's compassionless black stare following them out.

'I'll make it right, I'll make it right,' Peter was whispering over and over. 'There, there, he doesn't mean it, he's in a rage, that's all. He's turned into a monster since Suzanna. There, there, my pet. It doesn't matter.'

They were in the bedroom and he was tucking her in under the quilt, stroking her forehead, pushing back the damp strands of blonde hair where her tears had soaked them.

'I love him, Peter,' she whispered when he came back to the bedside with a glass of water. 'How *can* I love him? How *can* I?'

'I've never seen him like this. He's got the wrong end of the stick—don't worry, I'll put it right. There, now, drink this. It'll all blow over, just you see.' He kissed her on the forehead and held her hand.

'It's my fault,' he said later when she was sitting up, her eyes gazing blankly at the opposite wall. 'I should have seen it coming. Trouble is, I thought you'd be able to handle him. You've always seemed so self-possessed.' He patted her hand. 'I'm a rotten judge of people, aren't I? Always getting into scrapes because I trust the wrong ones.'

'Oh, Peter, I'm sorry. I seem to have messed things up for you too.'

'No matter.' He tried to hide the crease of worry on his features, but when she asked him whether the debtors had given him extra time he frowned and shook his head. 'No, damn them, they won't give me any longer. I guess I'm done for unless we can get Marc to move.'

'So what are you going to do?'

He gave her a lop-sided grin. 'Obvious, isn't it? I'll have to wait until Bluebeard's in a mellow mood and tell him the truth. It'll be up to him whether he throws me to the dogs and I finish up in a debtor's prison, or whether he turns into a guardian angel complete with halo and big fat cheque. *Very* big fat cheque,' he added as a wry afterthought.

'You still joke about it.'

'If I didn't joke I'd cry.' His grey eyes darkened. 'I don't care about all that stuff, actually. As I've said before, it's only money. It's something else.' He hesitated. 'We're fools in love, the pair of us——'

She gave a half-smile. 'Is that why you've been going over to France such a lot?'

He nodded. 'I've had to keep it quiet for good reasons, and if I say much to Marc he'll really go up the wall. So mum's the word, all right?' She nodded. 'Trouble is, that night we started all this I'd made up my mind to forget her. I must have been mad for a few hours, and I swept you up in it too. You're so sweet I just wanted to throw myself on your mercy and beg you to help me. Which is exactly what I did. And you, being you and so sweet, said yes. I couldn't believe how lucky I was. Stupid me! I should have known the only answer ever is to stand and fight. But it seemed such a peach of a way out of trouble. And I genuinely am fond of you—that goes without saying, despite how it looks.' He seemed close to tears. 'The trouble is I love her in a different way. I can't understand how it's happened. I always thought I was the philandering type, but my mind keeps going back to her. I just couldn't keep away from her when I got the chance to escape from Rocamar the other day. I'd like to whisk her away on my white charger, but I have to settle my debts first. It wouldn't be fair otherwise. It looks as if my whole life is a race against time. I'm so utterly sorry I got you involved. You've a complete right to hate me.'

'I don't hate you. I just wish I could help you— properly, I mean.'

He shook his head ruefully. 'It's a hell of a lot of money—even I boggle at it sometimes.

'Oh, Peter, how on earth did you get into such a fix?'

He patted her arm. 'I'll tell you about it some time, but not now. I'm going to change for dinner, then later on I might have one last bash at the brick wall.'

Sarella wanted to eat in her room. She continued to be its sole occupant, even though Peter was back. Now that there was no need to keep up the charade of being in love he'd taken his things along to his old room in another wing. But when he came along to tell her it was dinnertime he persuaded her to come down. 'You can't leave me to enter the lion's den alone! Let's at least show a united front.'

Reluctantly she did as he wished.

They were in the breakfast-room again, a log fire blazing, a table set for three, and, until Marc came in, candlelit.

'Why the hell can't we have some proper light in here?' he complained as he strode in, snapping on the electric lights and going round dousing the candles.

All through the meal he picked at his food, while Peter ate heartily with a quip about being a condemned man. Sarella couldn't eat a morsel of anything. It was as if things were taking place at a distance, in some dream-like realm. Surely any minute she would wake up and find Marc lying beside her, his arms holding her in the loving way of barely twelve hours ago?

He assiduously avoided her glance all through dinner, and as soon as the coffee was served he got to his feet. But Peter rose at the same moment. 'I'm dog-tired after that trek this afternoon,' he announced with a brief compassionate glance at Sarella. 'Why don't you two talk things over?' Obviously he had judged it unpropitious to broach the subject of his own predicament right now. Before Marc or even Sarella could protest he left the room.

'Talk things over?' queried Marc sardonically, going over to the fireplace. 'What can he imagine we have to say to each other?' He stood with his back to the fire, dominating the room and as if trying at the same time to dominate Sarella's thoughts.

Something in her strengthened. What he had done was not right, whatever the rules of the game. She told him so, her voice barely more than a whisper, but firm in its condemnation.

'You can't tell me you acted from any other motives

than lust and greed,' he announced firmly when she stopped speaking. 'What else could possibly be involved?'

She gazed at him for a long time without being able to bring the appropriate words to her lips. Even when she managed to do so she knew he wouldn't understand. 'Feelings,' she whispered. 'All kinds of feelings. . .don't they come into it?'

She didn't mention the word 'love', because, after what he had said and seeing now in his eyes what he truly thought of her, she doubted whether she could love a man like him. It *couldn't* be love. He wasn't lovable. He was monstrous, violent, wrapped in some kind of vengeance that seemed to have nothing to do with her or her love for him or anything else in the world she knew. She couldn't say that. He wouldn't know what she meant.

But she tried, haltingly, searching for the words, praying for him to understand a little of what was in her heart. 'Why do you insist on seeing me in this horrible way?' she finished up. 'What have I *done* to make you despise me so much?'

'I don't know what you mean,' he told her curtly. 'Do I despise you? Yes,' he admitted a moment later, 'I suppose that's fair. But I feel it's justified.'

'But *why*?' she cried, the words wrenched from her throat. 'I've tried to tell you honestly—I mean, it's no good. You disbelieve in me.'

'What am I supposed to believe, exactly? That you've acted out of altruism from the first? Obviously that can't be the case. Neither of you has admitted it, but Peter must have promised you something for going along with his mad scheme in the first place. That condemns you from the start.'

Sarella shook her head. 'It never occurred to me to

expect payment,' she repeated. 'I thought I loved him—that it was the right sort of love. We were friends. It seemed——' she shrugged '—a good thing to do to help him. To do something for him out of respect and caring. Something one does without properly thinking about because it helps a friend out. The consequences seemed irrelevant, too distant to consider. He knew I would eventually return to London and my career.'

He gave a short laugh. 'I keep forgetting you two are supposed to be bosom friends. What it must be like! How touching. I'm deeply moved.' His voice dripped sarcasm.

'Don't you do what you can to help your friends?' she demanded with a show of spirit, and when he didn't answer she went on, 'Or are all your relationships based on profit?'

He gave another laugh, its bitterness apparent, telling her that that was exactly true, though why he should hold so firmly to such a cynical view she couldn't imagine. She said, 'What is it that makes you so bitter, Marc? Has something happened to you to make you like this?'

He turned to rest his head on the high stone mantel above the fire and she could see the broad shoulders outlined by the fiery light in the grate. He looked like a figure gazing into the mouth of hell, and she shook her head to rid herself of the image. Even now, it seemed, he moved her, and all she wanted to do was reach out to him.

'If you imagine it's something to do with Suzanna you're wrong. I've squared my feelings in that respect long ago. I learned my lesson. As I told you once, we all make mistakes in our youth. I'll never make the same mistake again.'

'Oh, my love,' she breathed, unable to keep the words

to herself. He went on gazing into the flames and she knew his thoughts were too far away for her words to reach him.

Without prolonging the agony for them both any longer she got up and left the room.

Later Peter knocked on her door. 'Let me in,' he whispered. 'I can't sleep.'

'How did you know I was awake?' she asked when she opened the door.

'Is anybody sleeping in this damned place?' he asked. 'Sarella, I don't know what on earth I'm going to do.'

She put her arms round him where he stood on the threshold of her room. 'My poor pet,' she whispered. 'Something will turn up, I promise.'

'She'll leave me,' he said brokenly against the side of her head. 'I know she will. I can't blame her. Why should she leave the security of her family to wander the world with a penniless gypsy like me?'

'Stop it,' she murmured, 'you're dramatising the whole thing.' She was shocked to hear the tragedy in his voice. This wasn't her charming, flippant Peter at all. For a moment she held him like a baby in her arms. But just as she was about to tell him to brace up she heard an exclamation from further down the corridor.

It was, of course, Marc. Brow like a stormcloud, he prowled towards them.

He was barefoot and wearing a black brocade dressing-gown and looked like a Chinese Emperor. 'Are you going in or out, Peter?' he asked cuttingly.

'I wish I knew,' Peter answered with a lack of tact that made Sarella cringe.

'Why the indecision?' rejoined Marc. 'Won't she make up her mind? I can promise you it's worth insisting.'

Sarella's patience snapped. She spun to face him, and

before she knew what she was doing she gave Marc a resounding smack across the face. If she had planned it the blow could not have been more accurate.

'I've had enough of you!' she cried vehemently, not waiting for his response. 'Why should I care what you feel when all the time you behave like a monster?' she asked rhetorically. 'The last thing on Peter's mind—and on mine,' she added for good measure, 'is going to bed together!'

Marc laughed, a derisive sound, his anger making his whole body taut. 'Forgive me, my dear,' he ground out, ignoring the scarlet imprint on the side of his face, 'it seems I misread you at every turn—how extraordinary! I didn't realise my judgement was so impaired!'

'Leave her alone, Marc!' Peter butted in. 'I only came to talk. I knew she wouldn't be asleep after what you've been putting her through.'

'Criticism from my younger brother? How original! I take it you've managed to staighten out the wrinkles in your own affairs, then?'

Peter went right up to him. 'Look, I know I'm only a kid and I know you're still the big hero, but, take it from me, some things you *don't* understand.'

'Such as?' Marc didn't blink. He was taller and heavier than Peter, and Sarella could see he was itching to release some of the terrible violence that clamoured within him.

'For one,' said Peter, 'you don't know why Sarella did what she did. She's pure gold. If I weren't wild about someone else I'd be wild about her.'

'Do tell me, who *are* you wild about?' Marc's sneer and the sheer force of his presence brought a reluctant answer from between Peter's lips.

'She won't marry me until she's sure of me,' he stated flatly. 'She's ten years older than me. All right, laugh— but I love her.'

'Infatuation, you fool——' began Marc.

'Then it's lasted a hell of a long time. I've been seeing her for three years.'

'*What*? Ever since you were at school?'

Peter nodded. 'Ever since you and Suzanna.'

Marc gave him a murderous look. 'Of the same ilk, no doubt.'

'Not at all.'

'Look, pull yourself together, Peter. No woman's worth it.'

'*I* think so. Just because you're older than me doesn't mean you know everything. You'll change.'

'Never!' he ground out. 'I've learned my lesson.'

'You learned nothing from that episode. One day you'll wake up.' Peter touched Sarella on the arm. 'I'm sorry. This isn't your concern.' He gave a half-hearted smile. 'I'd better leave you to get some sleep. It was wrong of me to come running to you. I guess I shall have to learn to stand on my own feet. I'm handy at giving out advice,' he glanced at Marc, 'but I guess I do need to sort things out myself. Goodnight, love.' He kissed Sarella on the cheek. 'God bless.' He turned, pale-faced, and made off down the corridor.

Marc was about to go after him, but Sarella called him back. For a split second she thought he was going to ignore her, but he jerked his head round and his glance slid over her pale face. 'Well?' he barked.

'Leave him, Marc. Don't destroy him——'

'*Destroy*?'

'You don't know your own strength,' she observed sadly. 'When you make up your mind you go after your quarry with the ferocity of a tiger. Leave him. He's in trouble and he wants to sort it out.'

'If he's in trouble surely I'm the one he should come to?' His hostility was almost tangible.

'How can he?' She leaned her forehead against the edge of the door.

'What do you mean, how can he? I'm his brother, aren't I?'

She lifted her head with a weak smile. 'Have you really listened to yourself since he came back? He's in dire straits—can't you see that?'

'Can I come in instead of discussing it in the corridor?' His expression for once had lost that unyielding look, and uncertainty flickered for an instant in the glance he bestowed on her.

Conscious that she was only scantily dressed, Sarella gave him a weighing glance. Then, turning, she made way for him to enter, and went immediately to the window seat where she had been sitting wrapped in her duvet when Peter had disturbed her. Marc saw at once that the bed hadn't been slept in, but said nothing.

'What exactly *is* the trouble?' he asked stiffly.

'Money. He seems to be very deeply in debt—so much so that he's scared to come to you and ask for help. I don't know the details, but I think you should try to help. He's not a bad boy, just foolish sometimes, and he really does mean well.'

'This woman,' he said, 'who is she?'

'I don't know. He's been very discreet.'

'That's unusual—or is it? I don't know when I'm being told the truth and when I'm not.'

'That's your trouble, isn't it?'

Marc ran a hand through his hair and for once Sarella detected the bewilderment underneath the self-confident façade.

'So now,' she went on, feeling detached, 'what about *you*?'

'What about me?'

'It seems to me that both you and Peter could have

done with the friendly shoulder of a mother to pour out your troubles to—you're reliving something from your past. Why don't you try to talk and maybe get it all in some sort of perspective?'

'Don't come the little mother with me,' he said testily. He went back to the door and kicked it shut, then prowled towards her. 'I don't like being mothered.' He came to a stop when he was standing over her.

With the scent of him dizzying her senses it was all she could do to hold on to her common sense once more. But this time she knew she was in no danger of losing her head. 'What happened three years ago?' she invited.

'Nothing that wasn't both banal and foreseeable. . .'

'Well,' she curled up on the deep sill and wrapped the duvet more tightly around herself, leaving him to find a seat of his own as she knew he was going to, 'that sounds like life—so what?'

He gave her a flashing glance. 'Life. . .Yes, and I guess it kicked me in the face when I was already down. . .'

'So get up and start again,' she said roughly. 'That's what you'd say if it happened to anybody else.'

'Are you saying I'm easier on myself than on others?' Marc jerked his head up in surprise, all ready to do battle again.

'Looks like it,' Sarella returned, trying not to let him get the better of her this time.

There was a pause. I've lost him, she thought. He's going to get up and march out. But instead he gave a short laugh. 'Maybe you're right. You think I behaved like a fool?'

'I wouldn't know.' Now, she thought dully, he'll tell me about the woman he's crazy for. After three long years. She fiddled with the thread of the duvet, tying it over and over into little knots.

'I did behave like a fool,' he admitted at last. There was another long pause in which he seemed to be trying to choose his words. 'I came in for a lot of adulation during my racing days—groupies. How you women go for the glamour! At first it was——' He paused.

'Fun?' she supplied.

He laughed again. 'Yes, that. And it made me feel good about myself.' He got up and moved about the room, picking up ornaments and moving restlessly from one side to the other. Then he came to lean against the wall beside the window. She could almost touch him now, but he was frowning, running his finger over and over the Paisley pattern on the corner of the duvet that overlapped the sill.

'When I had the accident, that wasn't the worst of it. I could fight that—it was specific. I was barely conscious of anything except the will to live. People, even those closest to me, didn't seem to mean much. It was me, my survival, that mattered at first. . .'

He closed his eyes. 'I guess it must have been difficult for—for Suzanna to understand. I didn't recognise her for some time. I wasn't interested in her when I did. She was living—I was. . . It was touch and go whether I was going to rejoin her world ever again or. . .or cop out.'

He rested his head against the wall and fixed his dark eyes on her uplifted face. 'When she left me for one of the other guys in the team, somebody I'd kind of thought of as a friend. . .well,' he went on hurriedly, 'I wasn't surprised she'd gone. I think I wanted it. Her world was too much at that time. I didn't want it any more. I couldn't cope with it. . .'

He paused. 'I no longer believed in it anyway. But it didn't stop me feeling betrayed. Look,' he went on hurriedly, 'this isn't leading anywhere. It's all water under the bridge; you don't want to hear it—— I'm sorry if you feel I've been unfair to you. Maybe I've misjudged you, but don't you see, after all that, I can't feel anything for anyone any more? It finished for me three years ago. I had the blinds stripped from my eyes. Everything comes down to the fact that each one of us has to look out for ourselves, because nobody else cares a damn. Love, altruism—just pretty words. Simple lies we tell ourselves to hide the truth.'

He put out a hand and ran it possessively over her hair. 'I'd like to take you to bed now, but I know it's out of the question after all I've said. Last night you made me feel more alive than at any time since the crash. If I've been wrong about you I'm sorry. But you'll forget me, find somebody who can live in a romantic dream-world, somebody who can fool themselves that love is real. I don't believe in it any more.' He let his hand fall away. 'It's not me. I'm not the one for you. I'm dead inside.'

'Marc, please. . .' Sarella caught his hand where it tangled in her hair. 'You don't have to do anything. I shan't make demands. You don't have to pretend to feel—I——' She didn't know how to go on. He was shaking his head.

'If I'd met you three years ago,' he told her harshly, 'maybe things would have been different. Now I'm empty. I have no illusions left.'

'Love isn't an illusion!' she cried, gripping his hand, wanting to bring it to her lips. 'Love is *real*.'

He gave a twisted smile. 'I'm sorry. I no longer believe in it. I can't feel it. . .' With a final gentle touch on the top of her head, he turned to go.

'*Marc!*' But he was across the room in a few strides, and when he went out, closing the door quietly behind him, Sarella knew he had gone forever.

She flung herself across the room, beating helplessly

on the door, whispering his name over and over as if the force of her desire would bring him back. But the corridor remained silent, and with a sob of despair she threw herself on to the bed and cried till her store of tears was used up.

CHAPTER NINE

'You're thinner!' Beryl assessed. 'Don't overdo it. I want you for the West End after your six weeks in the sticks, and you'll have to have a bit of bosom.'

'West End?' Sarella had been back two days and her feet had scarcely touched the ground. Rehearsals for *Hamlet* started tomorrow, followed by a six-week tour of the provinces, and now Beryl was talking about another show!

'I thought I'd lost the West End part by choosing the *Hamlet* tour,' she puzzled.

Beryl shook her head. 'I've got plans for you. Tour for the experience, the West End for the exposure. Trust me. I'm going to make you a star, as they say in the movies. Now then, I like the new look——' Sarella had had her hair cropped '—and was thinking of putting you in for the *ingénue*, but I'm having second thoughts.' She stuffed a couple of biscuits into her mouth and leaned across the desk. 'Let's risk it,' she said after giving her protégée a thorough appraisal. 'Try for the older girl, the other woman, the one who gets ditched. . .'

There was a moment when Sarella didn't know whether to run from the office or burst into tears. She did neither until Beryl, her face full of concern, peered into her face and said, 'Oh, lovey, have I said something?'

'You know, don't you?' sobbed Sarella a few seconds later. 'You can tell.' And then she told her everything. 'And after he left my room with that bleak look on his face,' she concluded, 'I realised that was it. The end. So next morning I got up early and went to find Peter to tell him I was leaving. Poor love,' she smiled faintly, 'he was half asleep, and at first when he heard what I had to say he thought I was leaving him in the lurch after all. I told him I knew Marc was going to listen to him, would help him, that all he had to do was tell him the truth.' She wiped her eyes. 'He should have done that in the first place, and I should have thought about what I was doing instead of just floating along with whatever he put to me. Anyway, it's all over now. It's up to Peter what he does. He said as much when he got up and drove me to the airport.'

'Did you see the Voice before you left?'

Sarella shook her head. 'There wouldn't have been any point would there? He'd said all he had to say. He knew he'd been wrong about me. But he felt nothing.'

'And you? Did you say all you had to say to him?'

'No. I've got some pride left.'

Beryl looked thoughtful.

'Peter rang me yesterday,' Sarella went on, not wanting to encourage that look. 'He wanted to find out how things were going. He told the whole story to Marc, he said, and there was another row, with Marc calling him everything under the sun. But, reading between the lines, I think Marc's going to stand by him.' She dabbed her eyes again. 'I don't know all the details—it's something to do with a house Peter tried to buy for his girl in Andorra. The agent tried to swindle him out of his deposit and Marc's trying to sort it out. It's all up in the air right now.'

'You're well out of it, lovey. Now it's time to get on with your own life.

Sarella knew she was right, but it was hard. Something real had been left behind when she'd walked away from Castell Rocamar, and she felt only half alive.

There was enough to crowd out all but the most persistent of memories, however, for rehearsals were absolute mayhem, and from day one until the opening she felt as if her feet scarcely touched the ground.

They were already two weeks into the run when Peter caught up with her at her digs in Manchester.

'I've had a devil of a job tracking you down,' he said after he'd given her a big hug. 'Now, what I want to know is, are you coming to my wedding?'

'Oh, Peter!'

Before she could ask whom he intended to marry this time he said, 'After you left and I had that final bust-up with Marc I rang Marianne and told her she could do better than marry a penniless school-kid.' He grinned.

'She said, "This is what love is for—I'm coming over," and she set off for Rocamar and arrived at breakfast next day.' He interrupted himself to explain, 'I didn't make any false promises or give her a lot of romantic fantasy to persuade her. I told her the brutal truth—how I'd tried to buy a love-nest for us and got involved with the wrong property men. Anyhow,' he continued, 'the three of us spent the day locked in consultation, as Marc called it, the result being that he came charging to my rescue, routed the two con-mer-chants, who thought they'd got me over a barrel, and generally behaved like the perfect human being he is.'

He chuckled. 'It was funny to see those agents' faces when they discovered they were up against the famous Marc Vila! I suppose they saw their company name blazoned all over the media. I've never seen guys cough up so fast!'

'I'm so happy everything's worked out,' Sarella said sincerely.

Peter frowned and tweaked her chin. 'He hasn't been in touch, has he?'

'Who?' she asked, turning away.

'He's working like a maniac these days—some new franchise. Jetting around. He doesn't have a minute.'

'You don't have to make excuses for him. Why should he get in touch? We've nothing to say to each other. He said it all. I'm busy too.'

It was left like that. If she could fit in a few days' break in order to attend the wedding in Andorra she would, she promised, and Peter returned to Rocamar the next day, leaving Sarella to close one chapter of her life and get on with the next.

It wasn't easy. The success of the tour made it less difficult to tell herself that this was what she wanted, but it didn't stop those sudden down-swings when she was swept by a longing so total that it was like a haemorrhage of the soul.

She even imagined she saw Marc in the audience one night, his face just a pale blur beyond the footlights with all the others, but what would the jet-setting Marc Vila be doing in Yorkshire?

Before the members of the cast separated to check out of their lodgings on that last night of the provincial tour before moving in for a run at a West End theatre they got together for a few drinks on stage.

As often happened when a crowd of actors got together, somebody started playing the piano, and soon they were letting their hair down, doing what somebody called their 'party turns'. Sarella couldn't let the side down, and when she was pulled to the front she leaned against the piano and, after a whispered word to the pianist, started to sing.

It was that same song from the Dietrich film she had watched at Rocamar, and as she sang she found new depths in the words. They seemed to express her own helplessness, for it was true: she had been unable to stop herself from falling in love, and even now, underneath all the adulation and the triumph of her public life, her love was as rock-solid—and as hopeless—as ever.

When she finished there was a second's silence, then the warmth of the company expressed itself in a burst of applause. The director came to her as she sat down again. 'Somebody out front for you, Sarella. I don't think he wants to come in.'

'He?' Her heart leaped, then she took a hold on herself. It wasn't Beryl, then, so it would be Peter. He had told her he might bring Marianne over to meet her and to see the show if they could take time out from all the wedding preparations. While the party continued she made her way through the darkened theatre to the foyer.

There seemed to be something inevitable in the way her glance homed in at once to the familiar figure standing with his back to her reading one of the notices. He turned as he heard the door swish shut behind her.

'Hi.'

'I can't believe——' She bit back the words and took a breath and moved forward smoothly, a sort of professional smile stuck to her face. 'Is Peter with you?'

'At home, planning his wedding party.' Marc paused, expressionless. 'Sounds as if he should be here. Sorry to drag you away.'

'No, no, it's not like that. We're just unwinding before girding our loins for London. Next week's vital for most of them—luckily I've got a job to go to.'

'Was that you singing just now?'

She nodded. What was he doing here? So far he hadn't said anything to give her a clue. Why had he come? Was he pleased to see her? Had he missed her? She wondered if he remembered that time he had hummed that same song on the snow-covered terrace in Rocamar—it seemed so long ago now. Another life. Another time.

'Well, I happened to be in the UK,' he said briskly, 'so I thought I'd drop by and see how you were doing. Peter told me it was a show I shouldn't miss.'

'You mean you were in tonight?' She was glad she hadn't known.

He gave a lop-sided smile. 'I much prefer it without subtitles.'

She smiled inanely.

'I suppose you're fixed up for the rest of the evening?'

He was asking her if she was with anyone, she registered. She shook her head. Pride was irrelevant. 'I wasn't going to stay long—I'm whacked,' she said as lightly as she could. 'And on top of that I've got a date with the company minibus at half-past nine tomorrow morning. We go back to London,' she added in explanation.

'Fancy a lift now instead?'

'To London?'

He nodded. 'I'm driving back tonight. We could have a meal first, unless you've already eaten.'

'I'd have to pick my things up from my digs'

'That shouldn't be a problem.'

'I'll go and say goodbye. . .' The words came out automatically. She didn't offer to take him back to meet the cast. It was as if she couldn't quite believe he was really there. When she returned, though, he hadn't disappeared—he was standing exactly where she had left him.

Neither of them spoke on the way out, and the only obviously awkward moment was when Marc put out a hand to open the door and she bumped into him. They both apologised at once and sprang apart, then apologised again for over-reacting. After that they kept themselves at a safe distance.

They picked Sarella's things up from her digs, then

found a café on the ring road that stayed open until the early hours. It was the sort of place that had formica tables and ketchup in tomato-shaped containers. Neither of them commented on their surroundings. Marc wore a non-commital expression, and as soon as they were seated he reached inside an inner pocket and drew forth an envelope. 'Peter would have brought it himself, but I'm over here a lot these days.'

'You are?' She felt a flicker of pain. All this time she had been imagining him pacing the terrace at Rocamar. Alone.

'Aren't you going to read it?'

She scanned the wedding invitation, then slipped it into her bag. 'He's happy—I'm so glad. I'll look at it properly later.' She meant when she could concentrate without Marc's dark eyes boring into her skull.

'I'm spending less time at Rocamar and more time in London,' he informed her. 'I've acquired the world franchise for a formula-one racing car. It's keeping me busy.'

'In London?' she asked.

'Why not?' he replied. 'London's as good as anywhere. Besides, there was a thaw at Rocamar.'

'You mean the skiing's over?' she asked cautiously.

He avoided her glance. 'More than the skiing, actually.'

Her heart began to beat a little quicker and she waited for him to go on. What more was there? Thaw? What kind of thaw? His hand lay on the formica top and she longed to rest her own within it. Instead she fiddled with a paper napkin, and when he didn't say anything she said, 'I never expected you to come over here.'

'Nor did I. Still, now I'm here maybe we can see each other from time to time.'

'Yes,' she said, not trusting herself to say more.

'Good.' He picked up the bill. 'Let's go.'

He led her out to his car. It was exactly what she would have imagined an ex-racing driver to choose, but when he set off she was surprised at how carefully he drove.

'I thought you'd be putting your foot down,' she said, gazing out of the window.

'What about?' he asked, misunderstanding.

'Breaking the speed limit, I meant.'

He gave a faint smile. 'I thought you were referring to that episode at Rocamar. I should have put my foot down there.'

'I thought you did eventually?' she asked.

He paused. 'Oh, Peter.'

'Yes.' What else did he think she meant?

'He's OK. He'll survive. His girl's very sweet.'

Sarella closed her eyes. She could imagine the three of them at Rocamar. It sounded cosy. 'Do you have a flat in London?' she asked.

Marc shook his head. 'Nothing permanent yet. I'm still looking.'

She could imagine the sort of place he would choose. Something to match the car—all glass, steel, light, space. The simplicity that only money could buy.

Tired after two performances that day, she began to drift between sleep and wakefulness. It was painfully sweet just to be beside him again. After missing him so desperately over the last six weeks it was more than she had ever dreamed of to find herself suddenly close to him again, and maybe by the time they reached their destination he would have given her some clue about the way he wanted things to be. He switched the radio on and they drifted through the night together, flying over the miles to London.

* * *

The final week of *Hamlet* was a roaring success. Sarella sleep-walked it, unable to tell what was real and what was fantasy any more. Marc had dropped her off at her flat in the early hours with little more being said between them. He had climbed out of the car and, leaving the driver's door open, accompanied her to her front door to see her safely inside.

After a brief goodnight and not even a peck on the cheek he looked down, then said, 'I'll be in touch some time, Sarella.' He paused as if not sure what to say next. 'Don't know when exactly. Have to be in Paris for a few days. See you when I get back.' It was almost a question, but not quite. He said before she could respond, 'Good luck with the show.'

Then he was back in the car and moving away almost before she'd unlocked the door.

Three days passed without hearing anything from him. After that she shut him out of her mind once again. It was obvious he didn't want to start up what he had decisively ended that night in her room at Rocamar.

It some ways it was worse than when she'd fled Rocamar because now there was this new memory to contend with, and she had seen how marvellous Marc looked even in the chaos of a big city, away from the romantic backdrop of the mountains. Even when parking his car he looked masterly, totally in control. It's ridiculous, she thought angrily; he can bring tears to my eyes just by making me remember the simple things, like the way he reached out and unlocked the seatbelt for me—he'd done it with one fluid gesture, no fumbling with it—how he had flung his jacket on to the back seat with the same faultless grace, how he'd sauntered round the back of the car with a bemused smile when he'd winkled it into a tight spot. These foolish things, she thought, remind me of you.. . . And it was true. Every detail of their last meeting haunted her waking thoughts. At the same time there was also more steel in her heart. She had been honed by pain. And she wasn't such a push-over she was going to melt just because she'd fallen in love with a man with a heart of ice.

Stopping to pick up her mail from the box on her way out a few days later, she noticed the white envelope with the Andorran postmark straight away. Annoyed to find her fingers trembling, she tore it open. But it was a note from Peter and Marianne, making arrangements to get her out to the wedding. Peter could obviously read her mind, for, scrawled across the bottom in his distinctive handwriting, was, 'No excuses! We all expect you!' then a row of hearts and kisses.

Sarella concentrated on choosing a wedding present they would both like and an outfit she could wear again later. Was she going to go? It felt, despite the new clothes, that she hadn't quite made up her mind. But the new show hadn't gone into rehearsal yet, and the wedding was the weekend after the current show's last night. A few odd days of film work slotted neatly round that weekend, leaving her no ready excuse apart from cowardice.

Reluctantly she decided she must see it through, for Peter, and in some way for herself—she had to prove to herself that she could come face to face with Marc again and survive the ordeal.

Beryl gave her some advice before she left on the night flight the following Friday. 'Your destiny is here in London, Sarella,' she told her. 'Don't throw it away for anyone—you may never get a second chance.'

Her words were ringing in her ears as she eventually made her way through Customs. Peter had said he would meet her, and she searched the faces on the other side of the barrier for his familiar friendly grin without finding it. Then her heart did a double somersault.

Two soulless black eyes from out of the crowd by the barrier were pinned to her face.

It was Marc. When their glances collided he moved a little away from the crowd. With the coat-collar of his Burberry turned up, he reminded her of a private eye in a film—she was under surveillance, everything about him accentuated his detailed analysis of her appearance, and she felt a shiver at what it might portend. Did it mean he hadn't finished with her yet? Was he going to force her to undergo further manipulation of her heart-strings until she was completely possessed? What demon was inside him that could take her soul from her with one look? She tried to remember Beryl's advice, but already her defences were crumbling. She would die wanting him. The world could be lost and she would think it well lost if only he could love her.

She jerked her glance away and pretended to adjust the strap of her bag. When she looked up he had come through the barrier towards her.

In a dream, she saw him reach out and take her possessively by the elbow. Sheer nerves made her drop her passport. Bending to retrieve it, she had a moment in which to pull herself together. When she eventually rose to face him her smile was pure theatre.

'Marc! What a surprise! I didn't expect to see you. I thought it was going to be Peter to pick me up. Did you bring the car?' She swept past his outstretched hand and began to hurry through the arrivals hall, only stopping to look back at him over her shoulder to see if he was following her when she reached the automatic doors.

'What's the sudden hurry?' he growled, coming up beside her and again grasping her by the elbow.

'Longing to see darling Peter and his fiancée, of

course,' radiant smile still in place as she spoke. She ignored his guiding hand on her elbow and side-stepped it as if not sure which way to go. 'Is he nervous at the prospect of a real marriage? I hope he's still going ahead with it!' She chatted on, keeping up a constant barrier between them, all the way out to the car park, and when she was securely belted into the passenger-seat she fiddled with her gloves and gave a deliberate yawn.

'Heavens, what a rush!' she exclaimed. 'I came off stage last night and simply collapsed in a heap and slept straight through. And I'm still shattered. You don't mind if I sleep on the way back, do you?' In fact she'd had a brief nap on the flight over and the adrenalin was racing round her body, making the possibility of sleep unlikely, but anything was better than sitting like a frightened child beside him, hoping against hope that he would finally melt and utter the sort of words she had once yearned to hear.

Without waiting for his reply, she yawned once more, curled up as best she could, and, acting for all she was worth, let her head loll as if sleep had already claimed her.

Like this, she found it difficult to tell which way he was driving. All she knew was when they began to leave the straggling apartment block on the edge of town, because she felt him slide into another gear and the engine opened out with a deep growl, and then they were climbing, climbing, following the sinuous trail deep into a cleft in the mountains.

Long after Sarella felt they should have been slowing to cross the drawbridge into the courtyard of Castell Rocamar, they went on, the engine purring gently as they continued into the heart of the mountains.

Marc was moving through the gears with a touch like

velvet, his control so sure, so sensual that she understood at once the pleasure he gained from driving. It was the same sensitive touch he brought to their lovemaking, and the knowledge only added to her store of love for him, for she saw how he was the sort of man who was all of a piece, mentally and physically, a complete human being, someone she could only admire, despite the hell he put her through.

Shutting her eyes to the inevitability of what lay ahead, she gave herself up to the ride as he took her higher and higher into the peaks, following a winding route off the main road that was little used. Watching him secretly from under her lashes, she revelled in his evident pleasure, and couldn't help wondering whether he was driving so smoothly because he didn't want to wake her. . .or because he always drove like a man making love.

Shuddering with fear and anticipation at the prospect of the weekend ahead, she risked opening her eyes again. All she got was a glimpse of the empty Pyrenees, and the tiny concentrated ball of the rising sun, alternately revealed and hidden as they crossed from one face to another with first one peak throwing its dark bulk between them and then another.

Dawn in the mountains, she thought.

Something was beginning to happen to her, an excitement, a wildness that caught her by the throat.

Here she was at last with the man she loved. Nothing else mattered. It was a kind of ecstasy to be beside him. A weekend out of time. What was the point of denying how she felt? She wished the journey could last forever instead of ending, as it must do, when she stepped back on to the plane to London on Monday morning.

* * *

Eventually she noticed the changing note of the engine as they began to descend, and soon Marc was bringing them to a more sedate pace as he nursed the car over the drawbridge.

Sarella opened her eyes and, to avoid his glance, peered outside.

It was strange to be back.

The place looked heart-wrenchingly familiar, yet in several respects changed too, for as they pulled up below the main steps the first things she noticed were the banks of geraniums and polyanthus cascading over the balconies and frothing down either side of the entrance. They gave the place a summery look, an ironic note considering the winter that cloaked them both. But dawn had already reached inside the grey stone walls, touching them with fingers of amethyst, softening the austerity of Castell Rocamar and rendering the place almsot pretty. Sarella couldn't stifle an exclamation of pleasure at the transformation.

'You saw it at the end of winter,' Marc told her, switching off the engine and turning to examine her features.

'Before the thaw,' she agreed.

He gave her a telling glance and uttered a heavy, 'Quite.'

She played with her leather gloves, turning each finger inside-out then carefully back again, aware that he was looking at her in that old, familiar searching way that somehow held her spellbound, draining her will to push the door and get away. She found it impossible to collect her thoughts when he looked at her like that.

'I'm not a mind-reader,' she said eventually, then with a defensive jerk of the head she slipped the catch before he could reply and was suddenly free, breathing in the cold, clear air, turning her face to the rising sun, wishing

he would release her from the spell that still ensnared
her. What did he mean by that sombre 'quite'? Did it
mean something, or nothing at all? What did he want
with her. Sarella quivered with the knowledge that for
sure he wanted something again. But didn't he know her
heart was bleeding? Wasn't there one word of sympathy
he could offer to ease her sorrow at having loved and lost
him? Driven to such a pitch, by now she would have
welcomed mere affection—if it meant she could be by
his side some time.

She turned blindly towards the steps, running to the
top, leaving him to follow on with her bag.

He strode after her, dumping it on the tiles in the
entrance hall, and was by her side before she could
escape. His face was ashen. 'I know you're tired, Sarella;
you've had a long journey, but we're going to have to
talk.'

He was going to warn her to stop behaving like a fool,
she told herself. She put up a hand as if to ward him off,
summoning every ounce from her reserves to say lightly,
'Of course we'll talk. Why not? But not now. Let me get
a couple of hours' sleep. What time is the ceremony
again?'

Marc looked blank, as if uncertain what ceremony she
meant, then shook his head. 'Oh, that,' he dismissed.
'Midday. Listen to me, Sarella—can't we forget all the
things we said in the heat of the moment——'

'Of course.' She shrugged her shoulders in their thin
wool jacket. Tears gathered behind her eyes. 'All forgotten,' she smiled painfully. 'All right?'

'It's not all right,' he snarled. 'I don't know whether
you really mean it. You're different. You've
changed——'

'Of course I've changed since I was last here,' she
agreed. 'Let's hope so. I was overwrought, what with

everything that had happened, and, of course, so worried about Peter.' She felt the lie was unconvincing, but he seemed to take it at face value.

'I see,' he said, his face adopting that wiped-clean look that was a deliberte mask for his feelings. What was he hiding now? And what things did he want them both to forget? And did he really believe she could forget their lovemaking? Surely he could tell she was acting now for all she was worth? But he must never guess the truth. She wanted them to go on being friends—if this cold formality was friendship—because anything was better than never seeing him again.

She brushed a hand over her eyes. 'I'm sorry I'm not at my brightest just now,' she said, pretending to stifle another yawn. 'Which room am I in?'

'I'm sorry. I'm being unfair.' His voice was harsh, unlike his usual rich tenor. 'You're in the old room, I suppose.' He looked as if he was about to say something else, then apparently thought better of it. 'I'll bring your bag up for you.'

When they got to her door Sarella turned. 'Thanks, that's fine.' The bright, false smile flashed again. The door was open and she was almost through it, bumping the bag against it and stumbling a little. But there was a sudden movement behind her. She turned her head. Marc suddenly slammed the door back against the wall with the flat of one hand and was pushing inside after her.

CHAPTER TEN

'MARC ——!'

'Shut up, listen to me.' He was breathing heavily and pushing into the room behind Sarella. 'I've been patient enough,' he snarled. 'What the hell do you want of me?'

She held the bag between them, suddenly not daring to put it down in case it signalled something, the consequences of which she might regret. She drew in her breath, playing for time. 'Want? Me? What are my choices?'

He looked livid. She couldn't understand it. What had she done this time?

He gave her a murderous appraisal. 'Put that damned bag down and come here,' he gritted. He was standing just inside the doorway.

She put a hand up to her face. 'I don't know what you mean——'

'Then I'll show you, so help me!' With a lunge, he grabbed the bag from between her fingers and flung it across the parquet, where it landed with a thump before skidding to rest beneath a radiator, then before she could react to such a flare of violence he was reaching out for her, dragging her into his embrace, his lips ravening hungrily over her own with a fever of desire that sent shock waves of fear and desire quivering through her.

Too confused to respond, Sarella let him mould her beneath his touch until he ran his hands violently over her hips, locking her tight in a way that seemed shockingly intimate after the coldness that had preceded it, and then she felt a searing rapport as her body responded hungrily to his touch.

'Marc—please——' she whimpered as his mouth crushed savagely down over her own. He was oblivious to her protestations, his mouth stopped her breath and she tried to fight free, taking in deep gulps of air as his hungry mouth switched to her breasts. Her hair had been pinned up, and he brought it tumbling down around her face as he raked his fingers through it, then he gripped it in a bunch at the back of her head so that he could more easily drag his mouth over her upturned lips in a kiss that sent spasms of unwanted desire shooting to the depths of her being.

'How long are you going to keep me at a distance?' he rasped. 'Haven't you punished me for long enough? What do you want from me?' His black eyes glittered over her face to catch every nuance of expression. 'Sarella,' he rasped, 'speak to me. Tell me what you really want.'

He cupped her head in one hand and massaged her lips with his own till the blood pulsed into them. 'I'm going to make love to you. It's what you're asking for,' he ground out. 'I'm going to make up for all those nights apart. You've been driving me crazy, but now I'm going to have your body, and if it's the last time then so be it.'

He moved his pelvis strongly against her own until she squirmed in his arms, then somehow they were across the room and he was forcing her down among the silk cushions of the four-poster, fingers already lifting the thin wool sweater beneath her unbuttoned jacket, seeking the pulsing softness of her breasts with the mark of desire across his face. He held her face between his two hands and his glance penetrated her as if to see into her soul as he asked, 'Are you seeing any of those actors? Tell me! Are you?' A look that could only be jealousy, she registered, made his coal-black eyes glint with a hint of danger.

Then all at once she was swept by a wildness as if every doubt had vanished in a twinkling, and a bubble of pure joy lifted her head and made her lips tilt. He cared! He really cared!

'Well?' he demanded, seeing the beginnings of her smile. 'Are you?'

Sarella nodded. 'I see actors every day.'

'Bitch. . .you know what I mean. Say yes or no!'

'No, Marc, of course not. No. How could I?'

He ground his lips against hers again, forcing his tongue between her teeth, making her whimper as her body betrayed its need. 'You're not going to see anybody but me, do you hear? I've given you enough time to get over everything I've said to you. You're going to forget all that. Are you taking this in?'

Her eyes were blurred with a mixture of confusion and desire. Beneath the heaven of feeling that he needed her were the remnants of pain caused by the memory of how he had looked at her the morning after they had made love. She remembered the contempt, the ice in his glance. How it had shrivelled her to the point of annihilation.

Now she asked herself would the same thing happen again if she surrendered? Could she survive it a second time? She began to struggle, tossing her head wildly from side to side in an effort to avoid his marauding lips.

'No, Marc, let me go! Please——'

She beat at him with her fists, striking him in the face, making him jerk back his head. She pleaded for release, but, undeterred, he pressed more kisses over her heated face, reducing her struggles to a mere token of dissent.

He pulled off her jacket, then, gripping both her wrists in one hand, he forced her arms back above her head, and trailed his other hand over her half-naked body in a rapid exploration that made her undulate with pleasure, despite herself. 'No,' she moaned in a fever against the side of his dark head, 'don't; I don't want——' Then his mouth covered her own again, cutting off her protests and turning them into stifled, half-broken cries.

A clamour of conflicting emotions warred within her while her treacherous body arched greedily to every movement he made, answering each speaking gesture as fluently as if used to long practice. There was no stiltedness in their silent dialogue. Each phrase followed on from the next as if stored for an age and waiting to be spoken in just this way.

'You can't lie about this,' he rasped in her ear. 'You're not acting, not pretending now, whatever you try to tell me—this is real, this is true.' He swept her body with a possessive flourish, pushing her sweater up over her head and following suit with the silk top and bra.

There was a moment, as she felt the release from the flimsy protection of her undergarments, when it seemed as if something yet might stop him in the tidal wave of passion, but his intention overwhelmed any such hesitation, and with a moan of desire she put herself entirely into his hands.

But he was not content with mere physical compliance. When she was beginning to cry out for him, while he still hovered over her, taunting her with the prospect of even now being denied what she had at first fought against, he demanded her verbal surrender too. 'Beg for me,' he grated, 'plead for me, ask me to take you, Sarella. Tell me you want me. I want to hear you begging for me so I know it's real.'

'I can't——' she cried, shaking her head from side to side even as her body yearned towards his. 'You don't care about me—you just want another conquest. . .' It was true, she felt, for in the heat of the moment a voice was warning her that he was only moved by desire now because she hadn't fallen at his feet when he had followed her to London.

She tried to twist away, turning beneath him as he continued to grip her arms helplessly above her head among the soft pillows. She could feel his hot weight pinning her against the mattress, her legs helplessly kicking out as he began remorselessly to stroke her silken side, bringing his hand slowly and repeatedly from shoulder to hip.

'Say it,' he ordered again, his voice thick with emotion. 'You want me—I have to hear it. Say it so I can hear it.'

'No,' she cried, twisting vainly beneath him. 'Let me go, please, Marc, please——'

Where had the ice-cold man of the last few hours gone? His lips marauded again and again between commands to tell him she wanted him until she felt dizzy with desire and the need for survival. Her whole being was aflame and the cries she uttered with supplications to stop and to go on were bereft of logic.

'Yes,' she sobbed at last, 'yes, Marc, I want you. Please, don't—I want you!' she cried incoherently. She felt him hover above her.

His lips were suddenly gentle against her closed lids and he murmured, 'Are you sure? Please, angel, be sure. I'm half mad with wanting you, but it's got to be what you want too.'

'Yes, Marc,' she sobbed, clinging to his neck and trying to let her lips tell him what he wanted to know. 'I don't know what I'm saying any more. Just hold me. I want you—take me,' she whispered, twisting now in a way not designed to keep him away. 'Please, love me,

Marc. Love me. Please!' she begged, all pride gone and only the shadow left, the thought of what it would be like if it swallowed her up and he should leave her wrenching the words from between her lips.

It was what he wanted to hear. 'I tried to give you time,' he groaned into her hair, then, with a moan of desire to match her own, she felt him return to her, and then all the rest was heaven.

A little later he crooked her in the shelter of his arms and said, 'You've no idea what it took for me to come over to see you that first time.' He avoided her glance, and she saw how difficult it was for him to admit to weakness. He saw loving someone as weakness, but despite that he was forcing himself to go on. He said, 'I daredn't think further than that meeting. What I suppose I imagined was that it would all be plain sailing from the moment we set eyes on each other.' He gave a rueful smile and rubbed the back of one hand over his face. 'How wrong I was! You were like ice, and I was the same. I dared not say a word in case you sent me packing for good.'

'Why did it go wrong?' Sarella murmured sleepily, allowing her lips the luxury of pressing against the muscles of his bronzed shoulder in a banquet of sensation.

'Why?' he murmured, responding with a small movement of his shoulder. 'Because when you came out of that theatre party, despite singing our song so wonderfully, you looked at me as if you didn't know me.'

'Did I?'

'You did indeed. It sent my self-confidence plunging to an all-time low. I suddenly felt helpless. Like a child. I didn't know what to say or do. I was an emotional wreck.'

He began to nibble the lobe of her ear and seemed lost for a moment until she gave him a little shake to encourage him to go on and explain. 'You were Miss Iceberg,' he husked. '"Hello, how nice to see you" and all that.'

'I didn't say that exactly.'

'As good as. I was destroyed by it. My plans seemed nothing but vainglory.'

'My heart was racing so uncontrollably that it was all I could do to say anything at all,' she told him. 'I couldn't believe it was really you. I just felt as if I was staring and staring at you and that at any minute you'd disappear, like the ghost in *Hamlet*. Then you simply made some casual remark about being an errand-boy for Peter.'

'So that's what you thought?' He looked wary.

'You didn't try to disillusion me.'

'You believe me now, though, don't you, Sarella? You know now it wasn't like that?' His dark eyes searched her face, and there was a momentary desperation in them that made her reach up to reassure him.

He went on, 'I dared not come on too heavily in case I frightened you off. I wanted to see how the land lay. It wouldn't have surprised me if you'd given me the boot there and then. I'd behaved so badly towards you right from the beginning that you were justified in calling me an ogre. I didn't know how you could ever forgive me. I deserved to be shown the door. All these thoughts were racing through my head when I came face to face with you, and when you didn't show me out I couldn't entirely understand why. I thought, softly, softly. It was like driving on black ice.'

'I felt pretty much the same,' she explained as his lips began to run over her forehead. 'I thought I'd see how you wanted it to be between us. After that night in

Rocamar, when you told me you couldn't feel anything for anyone, I dared not hope you'd ever change——'

'That the thaw had really started?'

She nodded. So that was what he had meant when they'd met up again. Snuggling closer, with her hands twining in the thickness of his hair, she whispered, 'I wondered what you meant. It was the thaw in your emotions? I didn't know whether my imagination was leading me astray when you seemed to be implying something like that.'

'You've no idea how I felt when I first saw you step out of Peter's jeep that day you arrived at Rocamar.' Marc was kissing her lips, her nose, her eyelids and the secret places behind her ear-lobes. 'How could my kid brother appreciate a woman like you?' He went on, 'Not only love you, as I mistakenly believed, but actually persuade you to marry him? I seethed with a totally irrational rage. It was pure jealousy. You were mine—I knew that as soon as I set eyes on you. And so, apparently, did you! And yet you intended to go ahead and become his wife!'

He frowned. 'I watched for every little sign of a rift between you both. I longed to prove you were unfaithful to him so I could make him throw you over—I felt like a monster with every ungenerous thought that flickered through my mind. I was awash with ill-will.' He raised his head. 'It was like the past being relived—the same feelings, that is, but a different protagonist. Everything Suzanna had made me feel was alive again, magnified a hundred times. I don't know what I envisaged happening once I'd parted you and Peter. That I would step into the gap maybe. I was positively machiavellian—I never knew I could feel like that. I was out of control. I kept asking myself, how has he done it? What's his secret? This kid? With the woman meant for *me*? All I could manage was to haunt Rocamar like a beast with no heart.'

'Oh, darling. . .' Sarella reached up and offered her lips.

'When our eyes met,' he went on with his mouth scarcely leaving hers, 'it was as piercing as a sword through a chink in a suit of armour. . . Hell, I didn't know how to cope. You got right through to me in a way nobody has ever done before. To have been ice for so long, then to melt at the sight of my brother's fiancée! I thought fate really had it in for me. I set traps for you, and you seemed to fall into them—that is, you reacted as I longed for you to react, but you weren't supposed to react at all because you weren't supposed to feel anything for me! I'd got myself into a double bind, and there was no way out.'

'It was terrible not being able to let you know how things were between Peter and me,' she told him rapidly, scarcely able to tear her lips from beside his own. 'I longed to set the record straight, but Peter was desperate not to look like a failure in front of you. He really admires you, but knows he can't live up to you——'

'He doesn't do too badly. He taught me a thing or two—at first I was too pig-headed to listen. To have my hopeless kid brother teaching me about love! What next? But he was right about that episode after the accident when Suzanna and Raich got together. I'd learned nothing from it at all. It was safer to believe that all women were opportunists and all friends traitors. I adopted a pose of cynicism—armour designed to protect me from ever feeling vulnerable again.' He paused momentarily as he was forced to remember what had happened next. 'It was when you walked out. . .then I knew. . .my feelings were very much alive indeed.'

He pressed kisses possessively over her face again as if

to make sure she was still his. 'It was hell when I discovered you'd left that morning without saying anything to me, not even an angry goodbye! Even though I'd told you there was no point in your harbouring hopes, I somehow hadn't expected you to up and leave. I assumed you'd still be around. Knowing you weren't, that maybe you'd taken my advice and gone off to find somebody who could love you back, left me in turmoil. I didn't want you, I kept telling myself. You were like all the rest. My first assessment had been the right one. You'd only let me make love to you that night because you realised I was a better bet than Peter. You'd given yourself to the highest bidder——'

'To the Crown Prince instead of the princeling?'

He rubbed her shoulder thoughtfully with the side of his jaw. 'Something like that,' he admitted. 'And there was I, hating myself for being so incapable of shutting you out of my mind.'

'What was it that made you come after me?' she asked, curious to learn the truth.

His lips twisted. 'I had no intention of coming after you. It was the furthest thing from my mind. . . I don't like being proved wrong, and there was no way I was ever going to admit I'd made a mistake. It was Peter who forced me to see things in a different light.'

He kissed her lightly all over her face as if unable to get enough of her, and between kisses said, 'He knew exactly how I felt. . . After we'd sorted out his problems. . .he made a way for me to forget my pride. . .and come over to see you. He asked me to bring over the wedding invitation. . . It was a poor excuse. . .but I would have jumped at anything by that time. He didn't actually talk about it to me—I suppose he knows me well enough to guess that I'd have dug in my heels. But he cancelled his trip to England at the last minute and pretended he thought I was going to see you in your show and might as well hand you the invitation at the same time.' His lips came to rest on her collar-bone.

'Is it true,' asked Sarella dreamily after a moment, 'that you were spending a lot of time in London?' She pursed her lips when she looked at him.

He nodded. 'Yes, I was—I won't deny it. I really meant to get in touch with you again after Paris, but somehow I felt I'd blown it. At the back of my mind was the feeling that I would bump into you in the street. If it was meant to be it would be, I wouldn't have to do a thing about it. Fate would take a hand. Romantic nonsense. We might have gone on for years like that— me combing the streets for you while pretending to be there on other business! Each time I got back to Rocamar Peter would say, "Well?" and I would shrug and pretend I didn't know what the hell he was talking about.'

'Marc, I can't believe how easily we might have lost each other——'

'Don't, darling. Even *I* must have come to my senses before long. I would have come to find you again with my heart in my hand. I know that now. Nothing could have stopped me.'

'Even though I was so distant when we met?'

He sighed heavily and his face was momentarily sombre. 'I've been a complete fool, haven't I? I just couldn't believe you really felt anything. I was at a loss to know what you were feeling. Your beautiful, enigmatic face gave nothing away.'

'I tried to pretend I was thoroughly involved with my career—as I am, of course, but you know what I mean. I tried to let no other thoughts enter my head.'

'That crossed my mind too, in my brief rational moments when something told me you did care. I told myself, she loves me, yes, but she's having sensible second thoughts about getting something going with a washed-up ex-racing driver.' Marc looped an arm around her shoulders and pulled her to a more comfortable position beneath him. 'Even when you arrived tonight,' he told her, 'I couldn't see which way the wind was blowing. I decided I'd have to tell you how I felt after the wedding when I thought you might be feeling more moved to accept advances from a Bluebeard. But as soon as I set eyes on you all rational thought deserted me. My carefully wrought control collapsed. . .as you've just witnessed!'

He ran velvet fingers up and down her bare shoulder. 'I imagined kidnapping you, driving away into the mountains to some remote spot and forcing you to say you'd forgive and forget. I drove the long way round, debating what to say and do.'

'I thought we'd taken a long time to get here.'

'You looked so beautiful, pretending to be asleep in the passenger-seat——'

'You *knew* I was awake?' She made playful little biting movements down the side of his neck. 'I wondered why you were driving so perfectly. It was like floating on silk. I didn't want it to end ever.' She was beginning to respond to the tenderness of his fingers playing up and down her spine. 'It was a kind of torture because it reminded me of how you made love.'

Marc's voice was husky with desire when he spoke again. 'It's my own special paradise, driving my favourite motor through mountains at dawn, with you in the seat beside me. Say you want to do that again and again with me?'

'I do, Marc, darling. I do.' She sighed in a sort of wonderment. 'I can't quite believe we're here now, together at last. I keep thinking you're going to disappear, that I'll wake up and find it's all a dream. That I'm still rehearsing *Hamlet* somewhere and waiting for the pain to end.'

'Did you——?' He broke off as if doubtful about betraying the remaining shreds of uncertainty.

She looked up into his face. Already the shadows were receding from the room and she could see the darkness where his eyes were and the lighter line of his beloved lips. 'Did I what?' she whispered, half knowing what he wanted to say.

'Did you really miss me?' he asked cautiously, as if doubting her answer even now.

'You know I did,' she said at once. 'You might have guessed it if you'd remembered that night we made love. How could you have ever doubted me after that?'

He nodded, becoming still, and she could sense the probing from within the dark eye-sockets. 'I can't tell you often enough,' his voice deepened, 'how terrible I felt, how deeply bereft, when you went away. How could I have been so blind to have let you go. . .?'

'After I left here I missed you every day, every hour, every second,' Sarella told him passionately, 'I dared not hope for anything—it was as if you were lost forever.'

'I began to yearn for you the moment you left,' he told her in return. 'It was never like that before—jealousy and anger and desolation all mixed together.'

'Marc, there is one thing,' she murmured. 'After our night together, when Peter turned up next day, you were so savage, as if you really did believe all those terrible things you were saying about me—I don't understand why you changed so suddenly——'

'It was after seeing you and Peter in the cloakroom. He had his arms round you, bending to kiss you. I realised later it was only a brotherly peck on the cheek, but for one black moment I was back in the past. . . I thought he and you, both of you, had deceived me about your relationship—the way Suzanna and Raich deceived me for a time. Only this time the difference was that I really cared—it wasn't just hurt pride.'

'You know now there was nothing between Peter and myself except friendship, don't you?' she asked softly.

'Of course.' He bent to kiss her again. 'After I'd cooled down I knew I was being irrational.'

'And you don't believe I'm after the Marc Alexander Vila millions any longer, do you?' For a second her eyes searched his face in case there was a vestige of suspicion left, but he held her close, fingers running continually through her tousled mop of blonde hair, lips pressuring her face and neck as if he could never touch her enough. 'Never, never. It was madness,' he told her. 'But listen, it's going to be the other way round, isn't it?'

When she looked puzzled he explained, 'You're the one who's going to be the star of the Vila family.'

'My acting career?'

'Marc nodded, then his expression became serious. 'I don't want us to be parted from each other again,' he told her. 'I don't know how we're going to arrange things, but we've got to find a way.'

'We're together at last,' she breathed. 'Nothing will ever come between us now.'

'Are you sleepy?' he asked later. A soft light was flooding in through the tower windows.

'Not at all,' she murmured, 'you make me feel so awake.'

'Come on, I want to drive you.'

'Where to?' she asked, already clinging on to his arm as he got up.

'No particular place, just to drive for the joy of it, side by side into the rising sun.

* * *

When they returned some time during the morning, despite her lack of sleep, Sarella had never felt more wide awake. She felt as if she would never need sleep again.

Reluctantly tearing herself away from Marc as they went to ready themselves for the ceremony later on, she changed rapidly into the coat-dress bought for the wedding, then did her face and piled up her hair. After that she took out the contents of the red velvet box Marc had pressed into her hand that morning and put on the pearl earrings that had once belonged to her beloved's grandmother, knowing that now she had a right to them.

With a final darting glance to ensure that her appearance was in order she made her way as nervously downstairs as if it had been she herself about to marry.

'Practice makes perfect,' quipped Peter when he saw her. 'How am I doing?'

'So far, so good,' she smiled, eyes darting to the door with a yearning to see Marc again.

'And you,' he said softly, as she turned when the far door opened at last. 'I've already seen him—no words necessary. I'm so glad.'

More handsome than ever in his morning suit, his black hair gleaming with a brilliant sheen, and his eyes, his once dark and brooding eyes, now alight with the glow of love in them, Marc came swiftly to her side. He put his arms round her waist and hugged her to him, gazing long and deeply into her eyes.

'Get this wedding over, Peter,' he said without letting his glance leave her face, 'there's another one due soon.'

Out of the corner of her eye Sarella noticed Peter glance nervously at his watch. 'Ready to go.'

'Got your skis?' quipped Marc, lifting his head.

But Peter was already hurrying down the steps and didn't give a backward glance.

'Shall we go, Sarella?' Marc murmured in her ear. 'We can see it as a rehearsal for the final scene.'

And so it was, for they married soon afterwards and lived happily in London and Rocamar. Later, when Sarella was a star of stage and screen in much demand and there was time to pick and choose the roles she was offered, it was time to think about babies and eventual ponies in the paddock, just as Marc had told her. And then they returned to Rocamar, to their castle of dreams.

Next month's Romances

Each month, you can chose from a world of variety in romance with Mills & Boon. These are the new titles to look out for next month.

ONCE BITTEN, TWICE SHY ROBYN DONALD
SAVING GRACE CAROLE MORTIMER
AN UNLIKELY ROMANCE BETTY NEELS
STORMY VOYAGE SALLY WENTWORTH
A TIME FOR LOVE AMANDA BROWNING
INTANGIBLE DREAM PATRICIA WILSON
IMAGES OF DESIRE ANNE BEAUMONT
OFFER ME A RAINBOW NATALIE FOX
TROUBLE SHOOTER DIANA HAMILTON
A ROMAN MARRIAGE STEPHANIE HOWARD
DANGEROUS COMPANY KAY GREGORY
DECEITFUL LOVER HELEN BROOKS
FOR LOVE OR POWER ROSALIE HENAGHAN
DISTANT SHADOWS ALISON YORK
FLORENTINE SPRING CHARLOTTE LAMB

STARSIGN
HUNTER'S HAREM ELEANOR REES

Forthcoming Titles

COLLECTION
Available in February

The Betty Neels Collection

AT THE END OF THE DAY

NEVER THE TIME AND THE PLACE

The Patricia Wilson Collection

A MOMENT OF ANGER

BRIDE OF DIAZ

BEST SELLER ROMANCE
Available in March

DESIRES CAPTIVE Penny Jordan

NO MANS POSSESSION Sophie Weston

MEDICAL ROMANCE
Available in March

DEMPSEY'S DILEMMA Christine Adams

WIND OF CHANGE Clare Lavenham

DOCTOR ON SKYE Margaret O'Neill

CROSSROADS OF THE HEART Judith Worthy

4 FREE

Romances
and 2 FREE gifts
just for you!

You can enjoy all the
heartwarming emotion of true love for FREE!
Discover the heartbreak and the happiness, the emotion
and the tenderness of the modern relationships in
Mills & Boon Romances.

We'll send you 4 captivating Romances as a special offer
from Mills & Boon Reader Service, along with the chance to
have 6 Romances delivered to your door each month.

Claim your FREE books and gifts overleaf...

An irresistible offer from Mills & Boon

Here's a personal invitation from Mills & Boon Reader Service, to become a regular reader of Romances. To welcome you, we'd like you to have 4 books, a CUDDLY TEDDY and a special MYSTERY GIFT absolutely FREE.

Then you could look forward each month to receiving 6 brand new Romances, delivered to your door, postage and packing free! Plus our free newsletter featuring author news, competitions, special offers and much more.

This invitation comes with no strings attached. You may cancel or suspend your subscription at any time, and still keep your free books and gifts.

It's so easy. Send no money now. Simply fill in the coupon below and post it to -
Reader Service, FREEPOST, PO Box 236, Croydon, Surrey CR9 9EL.

NO STAMP REQUIRED

Free Books Coupon

Yes! Please rush me my 4 free Romances and 2 free gifts! Please also reserve me a Reader Service subscription. If I decide to subscribe I can look forward to receiving 6 brand new Romances each month for just £9.60, postage and packing free. If I choose not to subscribe I shall write to you within 10 days - I can keep the books and gifts whatever I decide. I may cancel or suspend my subscription at any time. I am over 18 years of age.

Name Mrs/Miss/Ms/Mr _____ EP18R

Address _____

_____

Postcode_____ Signature _____

mps
MAILING PREFERENCE SERVICE